Gov't Inspected Meat
and Other
Fun Summer Things

Gov't Inspected Meat

by DOTSON RADER

and Other
Fun Summer Things

DAVID McKAY COMPANY, INC. New York

GOV'T INSPECTED MEAT AND OTHER FUN SUMMER THINGS

COPYRIGHT © 1971 BY DOTSON RADER

Second Printing, March 1971

LIBRARY OF CONGRESS CATALOG CARD NUMBER: 73-120172

MANUFACTURED IN THE UNITED STATES OF AMERICA

VAN REES PRESS • NEW YORK

For Fred Jordan
and Tom Seligson

Parts of this book appeared originally in *Evergreen Review*.

The quotations from "The Love Song of J. Alfred Prufrock," by T. S. Eliot, are reprinted from *Collected Poems 1909–1962* by permission of the publishers, Harcourt Brace Jovanovich.

Gov't Inspected Meat
and Other
Fun Summer Things

chapter one

JUST got into New York from Evanston/Chicago, got in like a New American Immigrant, broke, owning nothing but what I wore, and believing Fun City to be the *place*.

"It's the last trolley stop," my aunt had warned me, referring to New York. "You can't go no further."

Down, she meant, thinking it Sodom, UnAmerican, choked with foreign crappers, you know the type, in her mind, fish carts, garlic, mandolins, prayer shawls, shopkeepers and loan sharks cheating the muted poor, spade rapists in Central Park with permanently erect, dripping, enormous dongs, gangs of them lurking lasciviously like fallen angels unawares in the Ramble (when in fact the Ramble was the playing field of a black children's crusade, tribes of dispossessed kids, unable to read their language, who made prey of the rich to feed the poor: themselves), hookers off Times Square, puss-strutting in stockings with seams, black chicks, with imperial blond and honeydew and vinyl-orange-red wigs, cruising the midtown streets with more class and honesty and, yes, compassion than the cake-eater bitches in the private clubs and the Plaza nearby. Evil, Evil, auntie would say, *a nice place to visit,* etc., where you made it into the life or you did not make it at all, *ever.*

In New York and hungry from sleeping three nights in the Port Authority Bus Terminal without a goddamn meal in my belly, on a wooden bench yet in the waiting room of the men's tearoom, and selling what I believed I would never part with—not again—for five lousy bucks to a salesman from Jersey who left my cock smelling of cheap wine and tobacco juice. In the terminal, thinking what? Thinking about my old man, and about Parker, and about my Jewish mother, dead at thirty-one of a cancer which took her breasts before, in pity, it took her life. And about my sister Lily, walked out on by me and by my old man and by my mother and even, sort of, by Parker. By every son of a bitch she ever drew comfort from.

Initiation into America: a dime a dozen, kid, nothing to it. I could go up the street with a quarter in my hand and they'd come running ... five bucks, johnny ... a dime in the hand, more boys than buyers, and the buyers aint hungry ... five bills, fucker, the chopper, mary, five bills. ...

Glancing down at his head bobbing in the lamplight, in the shadows near the bushes by the New York Public Library, and then looking away through the trees toward the street. I was *de*tached, like a fruit-picking pro, standing against the granite wall by the flower beds. Wet noises, for real. Coughing. Embarrassment. And when he touched my arms going down, when the salesman from Jersey touched my arms going down on me, lightly pressing his fingertips over my skin, like a buyer judging the quality

2

of cloth, I said hoarsely, tough (*coming out*, and trying
with all I had to pull it off with style), "Hands off, faggot!"
The pot calling the kettle.

The meat out, I thought of my old man . . . Mr. Love-It-
Or-Leave-It-America turning red, white and blue at the
sight of Old Glory, not because of any love of the land,
God, no, but because of what that star-spangled sheet
turned up in his mind. Insidious, degenerate pieces of
American myth caught on his rattled brain like feathers
on tar; sweeping decades of false hopes and lying promises
ladled out like bad acid in public propaganda, visions of
swimming naked in gold coins, real, genuine, one hundred
percent good, full-purchase-power dollar bills, millions
and millions of them lying beyond reach, if *only* he could
figure out how to unlock the door that opened onto the
capitalist yellow brick road. If only. A loser. Any way
you cut his life. A sucker for every wad of American b.s.
that ever hit the pavement. He used to call me Angel,
my father—the score is down on me lapping the groceries
and I am looking out across the lawn of Bryant Park, beyond the fountain, out to 42nd Street. The traffic and the
people moving. The marquee advertising: NAKED
WOMEN, THE FLESH POTS, FONDA PETERS in
PUSS AND BOOTS. The papers blowing in the wind
down the street. The porno stores crowded with casualties
smudging the photographs of exploited boys ($25, if it
hangs heavy, punk . . . now smile), sneaking honesty,
bits and pieces of fantasy, a courage in their famished eyes.

The hustlers in tight whites and levis, laundry packed
bulking around the meat, inside their mannered pose the
marooned silence, under the ass of Almighty America,

3

them, our countrymen, victims keeping it stiff, the lips, that is. They were the butchest, the most rugged, the most tried and losing, roughly beautiful creatures on the street; like a pack of Plains dogs, eyes sealed open and alert to score. The life, friend, the life. And I am thinking about once, when I was very young in Chicago, Illinois, the day before my old man skipped town he took me on a long walk to the Field Museum and through Grant Park to the waterways and the trails along the lake. We sat on a bench by Buckingham Fountain. We watched the fountain waste its body in the sunlight.

My father. Born in Los Angeles, raised in redneck country Georgia. A crop-picker dreaming of owning a business as big as Sister Aimee's, a machine more potent than Huey Long's. A preacher, an abortionist in Florida, an encyclopedia salesman (there he hit rock bottom), the dean of a nonexistent college in Oak Park, Illinois, selling worthless doctorates through the mails to public-school-educated, illiterate blacks; in short, a pimp for any product with the chance of a comfortable margin of profit, say two hundred percent. My smoothtalking sugarcups papa, a thorough, dyed-in-the-wool, everyday, All-American, total, collapsible failure.

Daddy, you were only true once in that you hated what you wanted to be, you hated the rich.

"Cost a million bucks, that fountain. Whatcha think a that?" he asked, bemused by the thought of the money. "Whatcha think a that, a million bills just to throw water up into the air. Some country this, got silver dollars for brains. Shit! Got shit for brains, that's what it got. No

4

heart. With little people starving and me out of work. Makes no human sense." Pause. "Listen, kid," intimate, conspiratorial, "if I had that million, boyoboy, what your old man couldn't do, if just one time those crummy, tight-fisted moneymen would unbend," he shook his head sadly at the tightfistedness of the crummy, tightfisted money-men, "what I couldn't do! Ha! If I had, say, only *part* of that money some rich thief blew on that there fountain," (he considered every rich man a thief, for he could imag-ine no honest way of making wealth except to steal it, and that meant stealing it from workers and poor grub farmers and the families of clerks since you sure as hell couldn't steal it from the cake-eaters) "Boy! what a hot property I'd be. You'd see your old man up there with the biggies then, don't think you wouldn't. Yes, sir! Me and the President of these United States standing together like old chums on the White House steps, me given the Nobel Prize or some other kind of dandy medal by him, th*ee* Pres-zee-den-tay hisself . . . in the newspapers as big as life . . ."—afterthought—". . . on the *front* page of the *Trib*, the Prez and me."

There he was with me in that damn park with the times rough and fading and his hair going gray on him, his body battled by booze and weakened by a seizure of hepatitis he never overcame completely, and there were no coins to be had, and no hope of getting any capital in the Home of the Free and the Brave without having capital in the first place, friends were few (*few!* He did not have *any* friends), and memory stuck like bleeding nettles to his mind, and not even auntie could tolerate his facile line about the goddamn Big Ship coming into port any day

5

now, and any day now he would make the Grand Killing and set us up like kings of the candy mountain. He *had* to run.

He stood up and went over to a vendor. He bought a cotton candy. I stayed on the bench, dangling my legs in the sunshine. I watched. A tall man, a trifle slumped in the shoulders, six foot, almost as tall as I am today, skinny, his hair thinning, gray, dressed in a thick tweed (his only) suit with overworn, shiny trouser bottoms and a dirty collar—forever in a suit because MEN OF DISTINCTION (preachers, politicians, morticians, businessmen, and others of the type) wore suits and ties, a salesman's vice—getting old, but then I was young and he had always been old and impossibly tall to me. Tobacco and gin. Yellow-stained fingers. Dark urine spots on his trousers—he never shook it out good.

Buying a cotton candy. I jumped up and ran to him, anxious it might not be for me. He liked to tease. Up to the vendor, pulling on Father's pant leg.

The vendor said that I was very pretty for a little boy. That I already knew. Father said, "You are, Angel."

In the park, a lady with a fur stole. Carnalfaced lady with a fur stole. "What a daahling child!" And my old man said, "That you are, Angel."

He bought me hot dogs and soda. At night we took the El out to Riverside Park, he sipping a glass flask of gin on the way, getting high and giddy, and into the black frights and, another swig, out again. We did the roller coaster together—good to me that night, despite the gin—for he was running the next morning, inside his gut as we shot up and down, inside there was the resolve to flee

6

and to keep it to himself, his resolve, and in his mind dark things, Southern, Only-in-America kind of things like seeing two nigger bucks hanged from a tree in Georgia, as a kid, seeing the bodies days old and stiff and stinking in the hot breeze and swinging from the Dixie LawanOrder tree. And the local sheriff doing the LawanOrder bit by directing the tourist traffic ("Mornin', folks, y'all come and see the darkies agin, y'heah?") around the tree, keeping the lily-white brats out of them branches and positioning the crowd so that what they hurled at the dead niggers wouldn't hit none of the good decent white folks on the other side. I gripped the horse's reins on the merry-go-round near the center of the park by the water. He sat to the side of me on a golden, wooden love seat, enthroned like a Patriarch, his hair pinkly gray in the light, grinning up at me, looking awfully silly sitting there grinning so proudly at his only begotten manchild and running his left hand easy through his hair and winking but still set to run. "You ride one swell horse!" he yelled, and I was thinking I was Hopalong himself.

Later we sat together on a bench by the merry-go-round. He told me that the best thing in life to be, what a man should finally want to be, listen, what he should want was to own his own merry-go-round and squat at night beside it on the cool grass and watch the people line to pay to play his painted horses. Abraham advises Isaac. "Get yourself some pretty horses that go round," the man was *looney,* I was about six and even *I* knew he had six fucking less than a dozen upstairs, "and don't have to be fed or nothing ... round and round, guaranteed, respectable ... a nice, comfortable, yearly return." Like a

7

goddamn cost analyst, sitting there and telling me what I ought to go after, *Christ! what life was all about* was owning some lousy merry-go-round! "You work for that, for a pleasure machine like that . . ." searching for a more *impressive* term, "a *scientific contraption* like that, all your own. Cause you're too old, Son, to be safe in this world and Daddy won't be around no more to spread the waves for you." But, hell, that *was* what I wanted then, my own beautiful, swirling, jingling, jangling merry-go-round; Lordy, to sit by it, on the edge of it, outside it like a circus master and make it turn for me, sending the gold spinning my way.

Some grand old man, mine. Soft in the brain, and a bastard to boot, hightailing it like Lot rushing from the Cities of the Plain. He was a Christian, a dunked Baptassed, no less, a born-again, saved, redeemed, Jesus-branded washee in the Blood of the Lamb. That summer.

Waiting for the El. Him drinking. Saying, "I love you little baby boy, I sure do love you child, and I loved your old lady, you got to believe that, honey, I loved that woman, I don't *care* if she was a Yid, I loved her, baby, *baby* . . . ," took in his arms, took tight in his arms, ". . . and your poor sister can't make out the light and what . . . now *what*, baby, what's your old man supposed to do? Huh, child? What's a man supposed to do in this fucking country?"

Fifty years of age, once followed the seasons after crops. Picked until his goddamn hands were numb and his back iron stiff. Hunger he got to know under Dixie sun, hunger grown self-conscious and rapacious with his coming into his very own American Dream defined by Cadillacs and Hilton suites and Popularity which wooed and disquieted him. Hunger. Festering and eating into his natural patience in labor camps and one-night, dollar shacks and errand boy jobs at thirty. Grown until it threatened to become him, grown that big. He *had* to run. A girl baby. Me, the son. And, abandoned for good, Ma dead, too much. His gift to me: a sense of hunger.

My old man and me. Grabbed the El for the Loop, he getting drunk on the way, conversation turning into booze babble, most of it lost anyway to the rumble of the track.

"That the Jew-kid?" Alice asked, opening the door, standing like a moss-covered fortress in her pea-green cotton nightie, her hair in curlers looking like two-inch lead pipe—her scalp red from stretching the hair too tight, hair she was losing like a real man.

"That's my *kid!*" Father said, moving into the room, pulling me along after him. He pointed to a red, overstuffed chair. I sat in it and soon grew bored playing with the gold-fringed tassels hanging from the long switch cords. "It's his *ma*, God rest her soul, who was the Yid, *not* the boy."

"Oh," Alice said, perplexed, thinking in her mind one-half Jew was all Jew. Alice was Polish. What else? "He still got his curtains?" meaning foreskin, "or you let the Jew priests cut him up?"

"Alice, what the hell difference it make?" Father asked, plaintively, working to angle into a position to kiss his business partner—that's how she was introduced to me, as his "business partner"—but she refused, standing like a

9

trooper with folded arms, feet apart. Difficult for him to maneuver with the room, small to begin with, full of over-stuffed Sears furniture, the walls dark green and covered with cellophane-protected pictures of the saints and a couple of Jesus with a bad case of heartburn on his chest.

"It *makes* a difference, you lug, I got the neighborhood to think of. With the Jews, then come the niggers."

"But he's a little boy. He's my son, Alice. Mine! Only six years old, Alice. He don't even *know* no niggers!"

But to Alice I was a Jew and that was bad and my father, even though she let him ball her, could not quite rise to equality in her estimation because he had not only *screwed* a Jewess but *married* one, a Jewess who had then gone on to die on him and burn in hell with the rest of them Christkillers. Oy vey! And sired me. Another little kike to grow up and steal in time from the Polacks.

"In the morning, Alice," Father was saying, standing naked in the living room after covering me with a blanket on the couch, "you give the kid a ride to his aunt's. In Evanston. After I catch the Trailways."

"*You* do it, you slob! What you think I am, a ferry service for Jew brats?" She stood in the bedroom doorway, naked, too, the fat on her stomach folding in on her sagging snatch. "What you think I am anyway, aint it enough I let you shove it inside me, that's a money machine down there," pointing to illustrate, "I aint no charity worker, dummy... and you get it free. Let you have it when Rebecca or whatever her name was (meaning my mother), when the bitch was croaking away costing you fifty bucks a day to have some quack pump in good blood after bad. ..."

10

"Shut up, Alice. Not in front of the b-o-y." Gently.

"What he aint already heard aint going to hurt him none."

"He's my kid!"

"*Your* kid! Ha! Some father you. You let them Jew priests take his little curtains, his little baby curtains...." And at the thought of the surgery, old Alice started to mellow and to weep. "The poor little kid, he aint got no drapes to cover his little thingy, poor little tyke...and you *know* I don't like cut joints, what woman does? Poor kid, you made a little kike out of him." Weeping.

My old man went to her and held her in the doorway and then guided her inside the bedroom, the springs sounding. I lay on the couch under the blanket having no idea what I had lost to the surgeons but, swelling with grief over my loss, I started to cry.

chapter two

AFTER my old man rode out of Chicago in his usual style
—two A&P shopping bags for suitcases, in the heat of that
month wearing an overcoat with a sheepskin collar, a suit
and several shirts to save luggage space, a pair of button
oxfords tied together and thrown over his shoulder, kissing
me good-bye in the early morning in Alice's living room,
promising to return soon—my sister Lily and I were taken
to my aunt's place in Evanston, a suburb north of Chicago
on Lake Michigan.

My aunt's boardinghouse was a large, white frame Victorian mansion, the kind of house you see in horror movies
perched on the top of a fog-swept hill. It was painted gray
inside, with cheap touches like fifteen-watt bulbs in the
halls, coarse toilet paper, old sheets covering the downstairs furniture, rules against running in the halls and
making loud noises. It was a depressing dump, resembling
as it did a charity house for the indigent aged, filled with
old men and women whose names I never finally connected with their faces—mainly Swedes: Olsons, Swen-
sons, Hansons, Johnsons—old people who patiently waited

for death on the porch, in the parlor, lying on their hard beds upstairs or sitting staring vacantly ahead in the long halls, sitting there, my aunt explained, to catch the breeze in the corridor, dying as much of ennui and disinterest as of arteries plugged with fat.

It was Alice who hustled us into Evanston, depositing us like baggage on my aunt's front porch, ringing the bell and declaring to my bewildered aunt, "Here they are, sucker!" cackling and sweeping grandly off the porch into her waiting taxi.

Auntie stood stupefied for a moment. And then she asked, rhetorically, "My brother's brats, yes?" opening wide the screen door, her face expressing helpless despair, her voice unpleasant, coated with the bitterness of her fate, high, shrill, frazzled.

Sister Lily moved ahead, I trundling behind her, my arms enfolding her, guiding her over the doorstep.

"She can't see," auntie observed, perplexed and growing angry as the permanence of our visit began to sink in. "Here for good," she sighed, watching us move into the foyer ignoring her, sister Lily crawling around the floor feeling out the premises, playing with the umbrellas in the walnut stand, making herself at home. "The baby can't see. Should've remembered," auntie more confident, gaining composure, the wheels beginning to turn, "... that *bastard*, that good-for-nothing *lout!*" pulling her hair, anguish, "*Two* brats, one of them blind! Good Lord!" Her eyes gazed heavenward, the last resignation, "Are the heavens brass?"

"You!" she said, pointing at me, "we have to make *do!*" and with that she stomped out of the foyer leaving sister

Lily and me alone to ourselves to continue the game of smashing umbrellas loudly against the oak floor.

In a few minutes auntie returned, waving a long length of cord triumphantly over her head, a look of immense satisfaction on her face. "First, we manage the blind one," she said, picking up sister Lily and lugging her, like a piglet to market, under her arm, through the kitchen and out into the backyard. She put the baby down on the grass and tied one end of the cord around her waist; the other end she secured to the trunk of a maple tree. Then auntie stepped back and beamed, her hands on her wide hips, and looked at sister Lily plopped on the ground at the end of her leash, her hands moving exploratively before her, her skin and hair yellow in the sunlight which fell in a patch around her.

Back inside the kitchen, auntie gripped my ear. "Come along, little man, we've got talking to do." She pulled me into a small pantry off the kitchen, switched on the light, and shut the door. She stared at me, as if undecided about how to proceed. I looked around. The walls were lined with shelves, fronted by glass doors, each closed with a padlock, holding hundreds of cans and Mason jars filled with preserves, fruit, pickles, potatoes. The room smelled of decaying vegetables and scented wax and reminded me, in its dampness and closeness, of a cellar.

"Okay," auntie said, "Let's get this over with." She squatted in front of me like an Indian, like Epstein's sculpture of Gertrude Stein, like Mount Rushmore, *massive*ly, her body giving off an overly sweet odor—jasmine and baby powder and lye.

She drew down my short trousers and pulled down my

14

underpants, none of it seeming in the slightest way strange to me, done before many times, middle-aged women dropping my pants, friends of my old man who loved to wash and baby me when the two adults played house. For a moment I remained motionless, intimidated by my aunt's size, or rather by the size of her head—enormous, watermelon-shaped, its contours distorted by two badly placed hill-like buns of hair gathered on either side of her forehead, each crowned by a tall, fan-tipped, silver Spanish comb; small eyes; cheeks like withered pears weighted and prepared to slide, covered with a network of tiny, scarlet veins resembling nothing so much as a road map of New Jersey.

Auntie hunched before me, studying my penis, fascinated, mumbling madly to herself, "Just as I imagined, that sonofabitch..." while I did a little dance, a la Shirley Temple minus the tap shoes and the ribbons. "Seen enough?" I asked, grinning and two-stepping around the pantry, feeling I'm-so-pretty, expecting the customary laughter as she loomed mountainously, like a dyke Sitting Bull, her ashen face devoid of humor. Apparently the dance combined with the nakedness gathered to her mind visions of Babylon, more likely Hebrew orgies at the foot of the Golden Calf, centuries of our family's pure, goy blood polluted by my father in one rash, disreputable act of Semitic passion, for suddenly she reached out—god-awful long arms—and seized me, shaking me by the shoulders and shrieking, "You're a *Christian* now! A *Christian!*" I wondered what the hell she thought Shirley Temple was, *Jewish?*

15

Sister Lily and I ate dinner in the kitchen on our first night. She sat next to me on a pile of phone books. I fed her with a spoon. Auntie sat at the end of the table, saying very little, not quite adjusted to the presence of a circumcised nephew and a blind niece gobbling her food. Auntie sat dumbfaced, crestfallen, several times mumbling idiotically, "You aren't a Jew anymore, you're a Christian. Understand?" Each time I nodded that I understood. "You aren't a Jew anymore, you're a Methodist. Can you say that, can you say Methodist?"

I said Methodist for her. "That's good," she said. "Say it again, so you get used to it."

"Methodist."

"You both going to Sunday school up at the church, starting next Sunday. You understand?"

Again I nodded, not knowing what a Sunday school was, never having attended one.

"You're going to be raised as Christian ladies and gentlemen, whether you goddamn like it or not."

"Yes, auntie," I agreed happily, passing my plate for more food.

"Goddamn right!" she replied.

Every Sunday for two months we were taken to church, thereafter our attendance flagged and finally failed altogether. Auntie was a late sleeper, what with her "woman's headaches," and her night prowls inspecting the house, checking out the boarders for violations of the rules. She wasn't much of a Christian, auntie wasn't; however much she tried to make a believable charade out of her religiosity her Christianity was altogether too pragmatic, too American in variety, to provide the necessary faithfulness to greet the Sabbath in a pew. Her public piety was established for business reasons. Evanston, being the Midwestern Geneva (Rome was located somewhere in the Polish section of Milwaukee), having more churches per capita (and thus more property taxes) than any other city of comparable size in the universe, being the headquarters of the Methodist Church, and the National Council of Churches, *and* the Women's Christian Temperance Union, that being the lay of the land auntie played by the rules. No radio on Sundays, no booze (except her own, under doctor's orders, naturally) no reading newspapers on the Sabbath, no women, no gaming.

Auntie was a fiend for order—she *ran* her boarders in squads for meals, timing them at exactly twenty minutes from soup to dessert (*always* tutti-frutti ice cream) toilet time was limited to six minutes, enough for any healthy person, use of the porch was restricted to "respectable members of the house" (those in the fifteen-dollar-and-above rooms) and the family. That was us, sister Lily, auntie and me. Some family.

At night I read to sister Lily from the Children's Golden Book Bible and from Disney fairy story books. In telling the stories my mind would drift into my own bloody fantasies of the demise of auntie at the hands of the Little Tailor, or some previously incompetent, itinerant, down-at-the-heels Prince who would plant one neat, Davidic missile for King and Country at the center of the old battle-axe's forehead. It never happened. Auntie, like the government, went on forever.

One night, when sister Lily was asleep, I went over to the window seat in our upstairs bedroom and looked out across the snow-covered yard to the filling station where the Shell sign revolved like a misshapen moon in the evening sky above the icy trees. I was thinking about my old man and my mother and about how much I hated the boardinghouse and the town and about how sometimes I hated sister Lily too. I wanted to escape. That night auntie came creeping into the room. "Psst!" she stood near the bed in the light from the hallway waving at me, trying not to wake sister Lily. "Come downstairs," she whispered.

In her bedroom, the windows open in the winter time, auntie lying on the bed dressed in a nightie and a Scotch plaid wool robe, like hunters wear, men's socks and oxford shoes on her feet. A lady trucker, sleeping in her shoes yet.

"Can I close the window?" I asked, freezing in my pyjamas.

"Close the window? Close the window? Are you mad? Breathe deep, breathe deep . . . mmmm, good for the lungs."

"It's *cold!*"

"It's *heal*thy! Not enough fresh air in this house, nowhere near enough. Like a mausoleum, if you ask me."

"What you want, auntie?" cautiously. It was the first time I had been in her room.

Auntie smiled and picked up a nail file and proceeded to manicure her nails. "All things change, boy," she said, filing away. "All that comes must go, nothing stays the same."

"So?"

She laid down the file. "Sister Lily leaves tomorrow,"

18

she announced, pleased with herself, and hesitated, refusing to go on, measuring my reaction. I said nothing.

"You hear me? Your sister is leaving this house tomorrow morning, bright and early. To a state school for the blind, where they teach blind people how to act *normal*, thank God. One less mouth to feed." I said nothing and auntie resumed her filing.

"I thought you should know," she continued, holding her left hand under the bed lamp, examining the manicure. "She won't be gone long. Pity. Nothing to worry about. Good for her to go, boy...."

She put the file on the bedside table and looked over at me. She sighed. "*I* know what it's *like* to lose people, to lose *men*...." Whereupon auntie began to tell her life story, never once looking over at me again, her voice becoming gentler as she spoke; I sat down on the floor and tried to understand what sister Lily's leaving portended, my immediate and deepest conviction was that it was the commencement of a purge, I would follow her into a state home—additionally there was, if unnamed, a nub of guilt exposed by the news, like the stump of a small tree remaining behind sister Lily, I had promised my old man to protect her, I had promised that, promised it knowing at that age that it was impossible to protect anyone from being taken; auntie rambled on about herself and my old man, as kids in Georgia collecting fireflies at night in bottles on the borders of a marsh near their house, my old man preaching in Atlanta missions and auntie stealing the collection as he kept the congregation of winos in darkness, eyes closed, praying; she spoke about marrying a farmhand she met on a church hayride outside Ames,

19

Iowa the first year she hit the North—*"beautiful it was . . .
I never saw the snow before that year, never, and there
he was, Devlin was his name, dark hair, strong, Good
Lord! so strong he could lift the front end of a Ford car
by himself, that strong, and handsome as Christ, I tell you,
and could he make love . . . it was Devlin who was driving
the sleigh and after the group was brought back to the
stable, he was unhitching the horses and rubbing them
down, we looked at each other and Devlin and me con-
summated things right there in the hay in the stable, big
as life, that Devlin . . ."*—she talked and I worked to picture her and Devlin making it in the stable and all the
while trying to keep my mind on sister Lily's going, thinking to plot some way of revenge—auntie spoke about Devlin leaving her—*"In Iowa! Do you believe that? Iowa!
Good Lord Almighty! what a place to be abandoned!"*—
talk about the family and their ways—*"runs in the family,
everybody this family marries, every one of us, what we're
good at's leaving the scene of the crime."*—in Iowa out of
funds and refusing to give way and scratching over the
years the money to buy the boarding house, and my old
man, doing this to her now, just when things were going
well, at this time to dump his kids on her—*"You've bread
and a roof, more than most. Haven't paid for none of it,
I'll never see one plug nickel, not from you or your old
man. You being a nogood like him."*

That is what she told me that night, out of the clear
blue sky, because sister Lily was leaving and I think she
thought the words, the confidences, would make up for
something. It happened again, too, one other time when
she was feeling maudlin and downunder, she talked to me

20

like that, she lying on the bed, I sitting on the rug looking up at her shoes. "See, boy, LIFE's a lone thing," auntie always pronounced "life" as if it were written in the upper case, "You're born alone, you go out alone, with the sweepings. You're alone most all the time in between. So, boy, when you meet people who are good, you have to be nice to them," thinking of herself as being the good people one is obligated to extend niceness to, "you have to build your family around them. Family isn't a thing of the blood, it's something of the heart," auntie said, in a trite way, her voice mellowed with banality.

Despite her quivering tone, I thought it was true, what she said, not as auntie meant it (as a charge for me to be nice to her as family)—true in that the aloneness was true and that the only goddamn chance to break it down was to build friends, to discover them, there in the middle of aloneness. But that also sounds trite. For me, at that age, everyone was a loser planning things which never occurred, distorting and attenuating and mutating in their minds things which had occurred, and in the distortion and the loss and the untruth dividing themselves from everybody else. My old man. Auntie. All of them meatballs. In some way, I thought, friends had to live differently, had to haul each other into each other, they had to make it stick and *not* run long enough to make it—life—good. That is what I made to mean out of what she told me. The only catch was that I could not figure out where one found friends enough to make it work.

As auntie had predicted, a social worker from the State of Illinois came and took sister Lily away. In the winter, it busted me up having to bundle sister Lily in her snow suit and lug her downstairs. "Don't we look *pretty!*" auntie crowed to the social worker, as sister Lily and I came into the parlor. "Wouldn't know the little tike was blind, looking at her, now would you?" auntie asked no one in particular. I brought sister Lily over to the social worker.

"He's a pretty little man," the social worker said about me, taking sister Lily off my hands.

"Sure is," auntie said, showing the social worker the door. "Good looks run in the family."

They left.

"Thank the Good Lord *that's* done with. I swear, boy, I don't know where the hell these social workers come from. Worse than librarians." It wasn't funny, but auntie started to cackle anyway. "Faces like a ram's ass," she said. And I said, preliminary to sticking out my tongue, "That's what *you* look like!" A Bronx cheer for emphasis.

"What, what do I look like?"

"A ram's ass!" I ran down the hall shouting in singsong, "auntie-is-a-ram's-ass-auntie-is-a-ram's-ass. . . ." I was learning.

For several months I amused myself with an inept attempt at guerrilla warfare against auntie, paying her back on sister Lily's account. I guarded myself around her, expecting to be the next victim headed for the state home, censured her with pointed glares, scrawled AUNTIE IS A DIRTY OLD WITCH! anonymously on the wall of the second floor bathroom, nailed shut the goddamn windows in her bedroom, spoke in garbled pig latin at the dinner table, declaring to the startled boarders that it was Jewish

I was talking and that auntie, to her chagrin, understood every word.

Auntie's response was on a level with my own. She simply counterattacked by calling me a "little kike," on every imaginable occasion. Examples: "Give the little kike more tutti-frutti . . . tell the little kike his *alleged* aunt wishes to see him." Auntie dropped the anti-Semitic barrage when the boarders began to pick it up, referring to me by her pet name. "Who the *hell* are *you* to call him a *kike*, you goddamn Norse oaf!" she said to one of the boarders at the table, "He's a Methodist, you lousy *pagan!*"

Four years later, in the winter, sister Lily returned home, confident, talkative, knowing how to do many things like read in Braille and walk with a white stick and make ashtrays and wicker baskets. I was delighted to see her. I loved her and her coming home was a form of triumph over the wiles of auntie and, more importantly, a triumph over something less substantial, more abstract, LIFE in auntie's upper case. Auntie, true to form, was not at all delighted with the Prodigal's return. In the four intervening years, auntie and I had come to a working compromise with each other, a compromise in my favor since it was premised on mutual ignorance of each other's habits. I had met a few friends in the neighborhood, the best of them a black fellow named Parker who was a year older than me and worked part time at the Shell station next door. He was at the house continually, driving auntie up the wall with his jive—"Hi, Big Mama!"—and with the legendary correlation between the color of his skin and property values. So, with her hands filled with me and Parker, auntie did not have much time for sister Lily, even if she did make cute potholders and clay soap dishes. Auntie remarked, at sister Lily's appearance, "One more mouth to feed (groan!), one more unrentable bed!" Beyond that she contented herself with telling bad Helen Keller jokes at the dinner table before the appalled boarders ("What's a Helen Keller doll do? You wind it up and it walks into the nearest wall!" Ha, ha.). In the end she disgruntledly resigned herself to her fate.

One night, after sister Lily and I had eaten up most of auntie's stock of tutti-frutti, Parker helping us in the raid, she sat beside me on the window seat upstairs and she told me she hated our old man for running out on us. She said she remembered how cruelly auntie had once treated her, how alone she had been and how frightened. She said she remembered how I had permitted it.

I felt very bad hearing sister Lily say that, very bad. I touched her hair and patted her arms, and I said, promises easy for me, "Sister Lily, I'll never leave you ever again. As long as I live. Never, never. I'll be good to you, sister Lily, never let you go away again."

chapter three

LEARNING, I was learning from Parker in everything we did. And we did a lot together.

In the summer Parker and I went swimming together in Lake Michigan, black and white like a Brotherhood Week poster, wearing our underwear in the afternoon and, if we made the beach at dusk, stripping down to the skin, in the water, in the night, skin bare and doing chin-ups and turns on the chains of the beach swings, improvising games. Did everything with old Parker, not only play—although he was great at games, especially basketball, where he could make the most beautiful shots from all over the court; maybe it was in the genes, the blood, his grace, his flaxen, panther elegance—took in the movies, we were both fans of cowboy flicks and war pictures, and hung together smoothing out the time ahead.

Parker was big on rule-making. Should have been a Congressman, for he could think up rules, good ones, simple and straight, for every goddamn situation you might imagine. Each game had its own rules. Each friendship. Loyalty was his Number One Rule. One had to be loyal to one's friends, regardless, even if that loyalty collided with other rules, that one rule took precedence over the others. "Man," he said, "friends are few, you know, like they're *rare*, they're valuable. Keep you alive, friends do." Keep you alive. And I was learning—done wrong by sister Lily, as wrong as my old man had done by us, and I was set not to repeat it. I deserved some points for that. Some credit for that resolve. If intentions count for anything.

One summer Parker and I made a basketball team for "underprivileged children" sponsored by a Chicago Methodist church. They had a regular league that played on high school courts in Chicago against teams sponsored by service organizations. "Little American League," it was called. Some league that. Gave Parker the shaft right up the ass. He was piss angry and he was hurt inside, bitter with an old hurt stripped raw.

"You ought to screw this fucking town," Parker said, "You ought to get the hell out of here before they kill you inside." That is what he said, sitting beside me in the locker room, on a wooden bench, both of us in jockstraps, our borrowed uniforms piled on the floor beside us, the basketball game going on without us, Parker burned, talking to himself thinking he was talking to me, "Chicago is copcity, man, those motherfucking cats hate you as much as they hate us niggers." *Niggers*, when he was hurt he would say niggers. Parker was the only black on the team. I was a nobody and Parker was a nigger, and the other team from Cicero would not play in a game against a team with a nigger on it. So Parker and I walked off. Not because I was an integrationist, or even political, although

Parker rapped about politics constantly. I stuck by Parker out of obedience to the Number One Rule—it was not fair for the coach to ask Parker to leave when he had practiced with the team for three weeks and learned the plays and was counting on the game. So I walked out. Parker was my friend.

We went inside the showers. "It's okay, Parker," I shouted under the water, "I don't like basketball anyway." Christ, I *loved* basketball.

"You're one lying sonofabitch!" he yelled back, laughing. As I turned to look at him I got an ice-cold water-dripping towel in the face. We made our game. Parker started hurling towels, and I ran out of the shower room to get my own to hurl back, in and out of the shower, grabbing towels and, out of ammunition, escalating the action to include the clothes of other players, and the coaches' pants and the referee's wool overcoat, and running under the water soaking them with cold water and chasing each other, laughing and carrying on, knowing all the time that our play was double, because we were getting back at the bastards who sent Parker out of the game.

We left for home before the half, the locker room looking like a water main had exploded in a clothing store, clothes and towels and wet shoes scattered across the floor, socks hanging dripping from the ceiling lamps. It was some beautiful sight.

We were in the garage at night where Parker worked, the place was locked and dark. It was the first time I had gotten laid. Parker arranged it. He in the back seat of one car. I in another. The place smelling of grease and gasoline and of a lily-of-the-valley perfume my girl wore. My girl: a dog whom I found wastefully beautiful, at least her box was beautiful, fleshy, wet, no amateur, hot. Awkward, with her lying flat out on the back seat, one leg balanced awkwardly on the top of the back cushion, the other dangling on the floor, I dangling in between, going in first with my face to get my first good peek at a real, live etc. and then the best part of me in, while she chewed gum and maintained a shouted conversation with the girl in the next car, whom Parker was fucking, about various boys at the high school, one in particular named Eric somebody who was on the football team, plus a running commentary on how the chicken (me) was doing on his first swim, while Parker yelled me encouragement and instructions from time to time, breathy queries like, "You got any questions, kid? Is it in there tight?" while all I wanted to do was hang in there like a real stud and keep my mind from remembering how Alice's snatch sagged and how close and touching my black pilot was to me and tried to forget my girl's face and think instead that I was balling Marilyn Monroe.

I was fifteen and three-quarters.

On Saturdays Parker and I often took the El into Chicago where he knew a spade chick named Doris who lived on the South Side, the territory with the highest crime rate and the least and most-on-the-take cops, in a tenement by the Dan Ryan Expressway, a really *down* building where, from the back of her apartment, you could reach out over the Illinois Central tracks and drop bottles and pieces of concrete on the speeding trains. Twenty-four

hours a day the trains clanked by the building, rattling
the dishes in the kitchen, rumbling through the community, their thunder passing as vibration to your feet
through the floor, as rattle on the back fire escapes where
small black children sat at night, like prisoners behind the
rusted iron grating, swinging their feet above the right-of-
way.

Doris was sixteen when Parker fell in love with her. For
good reason: she was pretty, tender, unprepared for life;
and this: wild body, well stacked, with firm breasts, large
nipples, taut, visible under the sheer cotton blouses she
wore. Her personal history was a bad trip, from the beginning until the end one worsening excursion into hell, ha-
bitual, habituating mistreatment. At thirteen Doris was
raped in a vacant lot one block from her house. Violence
grafted to her life.

The first time Parker took me to see Doris, she was sitting on the floor in the living room drinking glasses of
water, on junk, feeling high and good, the H shit a few
hours inside the vein, warm, her brothers and sister playing on the linoleum floor building towers out of empty
beer cans and knocking them excitedly to the ground.
Doris was lovely, her beauty drifted and gracile and worn,
her eyes never seeming quite to focus on yours. At the
house with Doris was her girlfriend, Thelma, who was a
fanatic about black nationalism, Marcus Garvey and
Mother Africa, hated, like Parker—Doris being hooked—
hated the bag man, the pusher, killing slowly.

Doris glanced up as we walked in, grinned weakly at
Parker, he moving toward her, his hands before him open

to her, taking her body in his arms, "How's it go, little baby?"

She giggled, her head rolling, her hands and arms limp, her body slumped and doelike. "Oh, lover," she whispered, sounding tired and at peace, "I'm so dry. They cut it with too much, too much . . ." her speech dying off in stoned fatigue. Quinine, drying her insides.

Parker sat down on the floor and held her in his arms. He said no more, only supported her, caressing her hair; she asked many times that he scratch her face or back or limbs, the junk making her itch. I watched her for a moment, the two of them together in the flickering, bluish light of the tube, oblivious to the shoot-'em-up Western on the television. Fucking pushers, I thought, the goddamn pushers and the goddamn cops on the take. At sixteen, for me, that was a political thought.

Thelma came over, out of the darkness. "Hi," she said, extending her hand and wiping it ritually over mine. "Let's leave 'em alone, what you say?"

Thelma and I went out of the apartment, walking down the stairs, the landing piled with uncollected garbage, dark, smelling of urine and spilled booze and what else? Something fetid and decaying. "The landlord, the city don't clean nothing. We had a block party to clean things up nice, brought all the shit out to the street and the Mister Mayor Man don't collect nothing. Sat there for weeks feeding the rats."

Thelma and I strolled for several blocks past abandoned buildings, boarded up windows, vacant lots heaped with bricks and cement and garbage, resembling haystacks on the land. It was dark, very dark, most of the street lights shot out by the neighborhood kids; people were sitting outside on the stoops making conversation and, on one street, a group of black boys younger than me played stickball, disregarding the traffic. Thelma said that the empty lots and the cellars were full of rats, that derelicts were often bitten when they fell asleep inside. We passed a public school. Thelma stopped and examined the building. "Watch, man," she said, and picked up half a brick and a hurled it through a window. I picked up another and followed suit.

We went back. It was hot. Inside. Thelma made me a tuna fish sandwich. Parker and Doris were in the bedroom, the kids still sat glued before the television. Parker came into the kitchen. "Doris wants some apple juice," he said. He poured her a glass, putting in lots of ice. Thelma and I went into the living room and climbed through the window and sat together on the fire escape. One of the little brothers tagged after us and climbed over the sill and sat himself beside me. And there I was, feeling *white* for the first time in my life, feeling awkward with nothing to say, for the first time thinking I had my life pretty good and clean compared to Thelma and Doris, compared to the little children. What a life—being so poor, that house, and I was so new to it that I felt out of place and, feeling white, without ever being told, I felt guilt because, despite all my complaints, it was sweet for me, life was.

The fire escape overlooked the railroad tracks. A train came by and, when it passed by the building, so close you could reach out and drop cement blocks on its roof, Thelma shouted, "Sit back, boy!" at Doris's brother, I instinctively swung my arm in front of him forcing him back as bottles, cans, pieces of roofing came thudding on the train from the windows above. Thelma laughed. "Wait until tonight. All night the whistles toot. They pays us back."

We sat on the fire escape for several hours, edging closer to each other until I had one arm around Thelma and another around the sleeping child. Thelma started to shake. At first I thought she was laughing and then I looked down and she was crying. I tightened my grip. "Baby," I said softly, feeling strong and masculine, thinking about how nice it would be to sleep with her, sex was in the idea, but mainly *sleep*, holding her asleep.

"Shit," she said, "it *eats!* that what I thinks. They kills us, they's killing Doris-baby, they kills us on the street, everywhere, beats us, man, until we can't never win nothing. . . ."

"Hush," I said, trying to comfort her, pulling her close, feeling paternal, "Look at those trees, will you look at those handsome trees blowing in the wind."

"I get so damn mad, all the time, mad. You *grows up* mad, just breathing this shit, just walking them streets, just being *black*, baby, not white like you, just being low-down and black."

"It'll be all right," I said, not knowing how to answer, never having felt it, despair I suppose, not her kind, not the kind that breeds in the skin.

She went on rapping, her words angry, her voice quiet, the Southern dialect softening the bitterness in tone, "He's a little baby," she said, referring to the boy resting in my arm, "a baby. Can't have this shit no more, no more black

babies growing up to live in this filth. This is *filth*, man!"
She sat up, looking hard at me, swinging her arms aim-
lessly taking in the world, "Filth! What would you do,
white boy, what would you do? Start to kill, that what
you'd do." Shaking her head, frustrated, beyond herself;
I stared at her helplessly, devoid of response, empty before her rage. "I tells you something," she said, grabbing
my arm, peering ahead, "we going to get ourselves some
guns one of these days, you believe it, and we going to
clean up the neighborhood. Going to get the cops and the
pushers, you believes it! Look what they done to Doris-
baby, just you look!"

"We'll get them, Thelma," I said, making another promise.

We took the baby brother into the bedroom and put
him in his bed. Then Thelma and I sat on the couch in the
living room and watched the television. We went to bed
on the floor, pulling the cushions from the chairs and sofa
to form a mattress. I kissed her round-the-world, exploring
in the darkness, and I entered her fast and hard, jabbing
into her, conscious in the sex of my white skin and her
anguish. It was not fair sex.

In the morning I lay beside her in the daylight, she
asleep, and played my hand over her naked body, fascinated by the contrast in color between my white hand
and the black sheen of her skin. One beautiful, tough
chick.

I saw Thelma about four more times until the afternoon
when Parker called and said, "Doris is gone."

"Gone?" I didn't understand what he meant.

"An O.D. Yesterday. Goddamn, goddamn. . . . Gone!"

An overdose. A junkie's very own special way of checking out. Murdered. Simple as that.

chapter four

ONE afternoon, Parker and I walked home from a neighborhood park by the lake where we often went to shoot baskets, having given up a year before the idea of ever making it on any team sponsored by a church, business, fraternal organization or school. Parker kept his shirt off as we walked, his body sweating, his skin very dark and tight, his back muscled. I wasn't sweating as bad, but I was hot. I took my shirt off and told him to stop and I rubbed his back dry with my shirt because he was really pouring it out down his back and the sweat was running into his pants, staining them. We walked on, he telling me about George Mikan and the Minneapolis Lakers as we strolled across the lawn up to the front porch to find sister Lily sitting there alone on the chair swing waiting for us.

"That you?" she asked, as we climbed the stairs.

"It's us," I said, going over to her and kissing her, her hands moving suddenly to catch my face in its kiss, to hold it there a moment against her own, her other hand passing gently through my hair. Parker alongside, leaning over, too, kissing her and she transferring one hand to his moist head, capturing both of us. She was thirteen. That summer.

Parker stepped back and, laughing, said, "Now aint that one pretty sight, though, with that pretty hair and that pretty face. Is *she* going to be some beautiful lady soon!" She smiled and blushed and lowered her face. She was happy.

"Read," she asked, "please read." Parker sat down beside her on the chair swing, pushed his long legs out in front of him and rested his feet against the whitewashed balustrade and rocked back and forth as he read. This is what he read, camping it up like a Southern preacher, one arm holding sister Lily, the other waving melodramatically and gesticulating in the air: *"By the waters of Babylon, there we sat down, yea, we wept, when we remembered Zion.*

"We hanged our harps upon the willows in the midst thereof.

"For there they that had carried us away captive required of us a song; and they that wasted us required of us mirth, saying, Sing us one of the songs of Zion.

"How shall we sing the Lord's song in a strange land?

"If I forget thee, O Jerusalem . . ." and I heard sister Lily mumble the words after him, a syllable behind, following his words, *". . . If I forget thee, O Jerusalem, let my right hand forget her cunning. If I do not remember thee, let my tongue cleave to the roof of my mouth; if I prefer not Jerusalem above my chief joy."*

Two months later. Night. Parker was running into Evanston early evenings screwing some white bitch named

Rosy Lynn Miller whose husband managed the local A&P, and was an officer in the American Legion, and heard one day from one of his customers about a black stud with a wet cock entering his wife a few times a week. I got a call at the house about two in the morning saying that Rosy Lynn's husband had gotten Parker down at the lake with a few of his off-duty cop friends on hand to help him fix the upstartin' nigger. No niggers in Evanston, only Bahaists and Methodists and Episcopalians and Reformed Jews and nellie cake-eater undergraduates at Northwestern and Garrett Seminary.

Parker's head was below the water, a rope tied around his neck to an anchor pipe on the lake bottom. The rest of his body floated up at an angle. There was a large crowd, mainly men, a few cops to watch over things until the coroner arrived. About six men waded into the water to get the nigger. Dead, and they could not leave the kid alone. They pulled down his pants and bent over him, one of them slipping in the Lake Michigan water and laughing at his fall. "The fucking nigger buck pushed me!" howling giddy and kicking Parker's body, while his fellow whites leaned over Parker's body and castrated him. The nation's night court.

The afternoon of the night I received the phone call at the house saying they had gotten Parker down at the lake, that afternoon I was upstairs in the house with blind sister Lily on the floor of the attic listening to the radio soft because auntie was downstairs in the parlor sleeping on the davenport.

One of the guys who boarded in the house—his name

was Jack—was lying on the bed where I was sprawled in the heat. I was using a pile of comic books as a cushion and I was hearing Jack talk. Jack was young, about my age, and an orphan and he *believed,* as some people believe in Hollywood things like happy endings and marriages-made-in-heaven and people flying like goddamn bluebirds somewhere over the rainbow, Jack believed that his *actual* father, you understand, was some Class A duke in Wales who owned a castle that boasted gold toilet seats and walls of paneled jasper and who was going to come clopping any day soon down Elm Street in Evanston, like a knight out of a Disney epic, and claim his son and heir. Jack wanted—like how many other buggerantoes?—more than he wanted to see his Duke of Earl, Jack wanted to be a *Movie Star.* American in that, democratic except when it came to the idea of aristocracy. He papered his walls with fan mag pictures of the Immortals and delighted in dishing about their love affairs, naming the directors and producers one had to open wide the tushie for to *make it big!* in Death Valley, California.

Jack kept an Old Bag Book where he pasted pictures of the waning numbers (Davis, Crawford, Swanson, Loy) at their worst, caught stewed, yawning, picking their noses, poses like that. But above them all, the hero he loved beyond words and measure, the one in whom he placed a simple, innocent faith was *Farley Granger.* Jack tried to look, dress, act, pout, sleep, *piss* like Farley Granger. He carried Granger's picture in his wallet and had another, reproduced lifesize, pasted in the bathroom across from his toilet so he could sit and cream at the sight. "Granger's got to be the most *stunning* male person in the entire

38

world!" he used to say, gazing into the bathroom mirror, limp with disappointment over the dearth of physical similarity.

But Granger was more than simply an actor, Farley Granger was a moral principle, a state religion, a national myth. When Jack was confronted by some terribly difficult problem (say, knowing my aunt's aversion to cats, should he continue to place them, tied together at the tail, in her bureau drawers? What was the *Answer* to war? Would excessive brushing make his hair fall out?) he would pause a moment, assume a prayerful attitude, and ask himself that eternal question: what would Farley Granger *do?*

While Lily and I and especially Parker (who thought Jack was one spaced cat) liked Jack, my aunt detested him. If it were not for the fact that he paid, on time, twice the going rate for his room, she would have tossed out the son of a bitch long ago. She *loathed* Jack for some very logical and eminently Christian reasons: for one thing, he was too handsome and she did not trust young men who were too handsome; also she did not appreciate his camping around the neighborhood in sailor suits or loincloths pretending he was Farley Granger on location; she did not like his borrowing her Passion-In-Paris brand makeup, manufactured in Brooklyn, U.S.A., even if *Silver Screen* magazine had written that the Great Man had used the stuff in his last flick; and she did not like his cats.

Jack brought home stray cats, scrawny, foul-tempered, tacky alley toms, and hid them in his room until the odor brought my aunt roaring up the stairs—her carriage often unsteady because of the whiskey she belted down to relieve her daily monthly woman's headaches—shouting that

39

she was going to cast him and his goddamn hair-shedding, plague-carrying cats out of the goddamn house. God*damn!* Every few weeks she and Jack argued over the strays, fighting their way down the steps, Jack clinging pathetically to her dress and appealing to her higher, humanitarian instincts, the batch of cats, several caught by the nape of the neck in each hand, screaming and hissing and scratching, and my aunt yelling at Jack to let go of her goddamn dress, convinced that the cats carried deadly diseases into the house, a positive menace to the public health. And he, Farley Granger at his most emotive moment, crying hysterically, with great, melodramatic gestures, "Madame, thou art wicked and unnatural!" Unreal.

But that afternoon, the afternoon of Parker's night, I was in Jack's room with Lily playing the radio on the floor. He was trying to decide whether to go to Manhattan or Hollywood to be Discovered, his quandary arising because he could not determine where Granger was working that summer.

Jack lay on the bed, his shirt off, beautifully built, the sunlight coming in through the gauze curtains of the windows and hitting his eyes softly and making the blue of his eyes seem fathomless and pure, the radio playing, and sister Lily singing along. I lay beside him on a pile of movie magazines and comic books and listened to him speak about the Great White Way and his STAR written in sparkling, mirrored glass over the dressing room door. I listened bewitched. He believed very much what he told me and I was tripping inside his dream games, the castle in Wales, the duke, the wealth and wonder of being an All-American Top Box Office Star, a world pressed eter-

nally on celluloid that never knew a real war or real death
or real hunger or pain that really hurt. An American
heaven. Man, it was *good* to invent families, us triumphant
with the generosity of kings, of boys before America's
easily spilled blood, touted, taxed and forgotten, spread
into our lives. Jack rambled on, imagining in the sunshine
—crystal and gold and silver and sapphire and chalcedony
and emerald and sardonyx and sardius and chrysolite and
beryl and topaz and chrysoprasus and jacinth and ame-
thyst—hands moving in the air above him building visions
of his improbable future, telling me that there was nothing one could not do in order to refuse a life of poverty
and obscurity, that there was nothing worse than living
poor, unstarred in the United States, even if you were a
duke's son and heir and had a magnificent, ivy-covered
castle in Wales you had never seen, there was nothing
worse in America than being a nothingburger in America.
Kid, there aint nothing worse.

Lily asked, "Where's Parker?" He being on her mind
most all the time. She was loved by Parker and loved him
in return. Being blind, she was no racist.

"Jesus! Is *Parker* going to get *his* tonight!" Jack exclaimed, laughing at the thought. He was jealous of Parker, I think, and he was, in a mild way, a racist.

"What?" Lily asked, lifting her face up, her eyes wide
open and seeing nothing but those eyes seeming startled
and wondering, "What you say about Parker?"

"I *said* that colored boy is going to get *his* tonight."

"What's that mean?" she asked, confused.

"Don't mean nothing, Lily," I said, suspecting, even

41

before Jack had spoken, that Parker was in for the shit. Rumors around town about him and Rosy Lynn.

That was the warning. That, and the fact that later in the evening, with Lily downstairs, Jack said, "You know they're planning to screw him good tonight, Rosy Lynn's husband is. You know that?"

"Yeah," I said brusquely. Even though I did *not* know it I would never admit to Jack, he being a fag, that I did not know something he knew about my friends, my male friends, "It aint true," I said, knowing in my gut that it was true, but if I admitted its truth having to go and warn Parker at the filling station where he worked. That I could not do. So I did not warn my friend.

Parker's head was below the water. And I did not warn my friend.

When I told sister Lily about Parker being murdered at the lake, she did not say anything, she remained sitting in the dark parlor with the shades drawn to keep the coolness inside. Later she walked out onto the porch and sat down beside me on the chair swing, both of us thinking about Parker. She rocked on the swing, the Bible in her hand, holding the damn thing upside down on her lap and pretending that it was a Braille Bible instead of it being what it was, just an ordinary sighted people's kind of Bible; she opened it up and pretending ran her fingers along the page, her head down, her hair falling around her face, and mumbled the psalm over and over, *"If I forget thee, O Jerusalem. . . ."* but the meaning in her Jerusalem was the feel of Parker's voice and face.

In New York I did the street, having to run from Evanston after it was no good anymore, aloneness driving in on me, run from it like my old man, breaking all the promises, walking out on sister Lily without a word of good-bye, in my head sweet Parker grinning and winking and laughing and reaching out and touching and making whole as motherfucking Miss Decencies—American Legion variety —made set to curse and leap, grabbing his glory in time as sure as three hundred years of slave pain won't make you free, black countrymen, that sure, grabbing in the American Eagle talon my friend's hidden treasure, tropical orchids, onyx diamonds, you name it, his ballocks' future and dividing him from it as he was, as a race, the victim divided from *any* future, however poor, where he was not the game of the hunt, the injured quail, where he was not forever the American nigger forever with the stench of boiling tar and thong and fresh-oiled rope in his nostrils. I had to run.

Reasons, as if reasons are ever known, I knew enough to understand that it was finished for me in that place, what with my head stormed hard by pictures of Parker meeting his angel without me, not one word from me, think of it! because he had said (we used to travel into Chicago and check into the Turkish baths and let the faggots go down on us for coins) that I enjoyed the game of fag-baiting too much and insinuated that I loved him in that way and I suspected it was true and hid from him, denying it. Pictures of Doris at the close on the linoleum floor needing the coolness, the skin on her face and arms crudded with sores from scratching, out of it completely as in a coma. Before I left I made one jab at producing the balance for Parker—I met Miller, who led the pack that killed him, met him in the street outside his house and smashed one heavy motherfucking rock against the base of his motherfucking neck. And watched him fall. He lived. The bad survive.

So in New York I learned to mark the basketeer on Sixth Avenue in the afternoon; did the bars as the browning queens made their nightly bird circuits, fluttering out like deadly veiled widow-birds, winged-faggot carrion peering for meat; I looked for a meal ticket for me—a one-way man—any size, height, either side of the street, and on the way passed something tender, gentle, soon expired unforgotten. I was learning. Hustling paid trade, and early I knew I had to avoid becoming an unsalvageable victim: today's trade, tomorrow's competition. I had to avoid hell.

chapter five

I HIT New York in the spring, taking a bus in from Evanston, ten bills on me—a gift from auntie who warned me I was doomed to defeat—some clothes, a sharp suede jacket, corduroy trousers and, in my mind, the baggage, which was turning sour like betrayal after the act, the multiple chunks of waste, the failure, colluding and riveting like an indictment, Doris slipping out on the warm junk, Parker landing hard, drawing compassion, after the fact, or at least remorse from me.

It was tough getting used to my past, the time and place and the acts, rolling it together like you bind a corpse, stepping back, passing far from it and scared of it, of repeating it, and scared, too, of the future, New York unknown until I walked into auntie's room—saying I was walking out, unable to climb the stairs and face sister Lily, blind and yet I was afraid of her seeing me, until then New York was off the map, not part of me.

Riding into Manhattan and thinking, I have to do better, hold myself in, remember Parker's rules, avoid promises ... watch for a time, how does a man live and make it truly without mistakes that cost blood, malinger on the edge and heal myself. And I remembered the sweet times with Parker and with sister Lily, and I remembered my old man, long time since the bastard skipped out and I remembered him now.

I think I was lazy. Or too vain. Or my threshold of boredom was too low. Or my love of sex, rather than love play, of pursuit and angled glances from the corner of an eye and gestures weighted with meaning, too strong. Or my conviction of futility too pervasive. Or my love of freedom too imbedded in what I was. I had planned to get a job. Simple. Eight million people in New York. Room for one more. But I never really tried. A job was authority, taking orders, marking time, being inside and observed by the boss in the afternoon when the last good weather of the year was growing thin outside, held in one place when you burned to be in another, selling what was passing fast too cheap. Hatred of authority, that and the sense that my friends—and wasn't that what made you want to breathe?—*friends,* as Parker used the term, were not signing work sheets and pressing time clocks, but were out in the street.

It took me three days of watching the hustlers work, running out of coins (*nobody* does New York on five dollars a day) and getting hungry and thinking, I've done it before, I can do it again, only score a few times until I get settled, get some kind of bearable job, a pad, a chick, hustling is making do. Temporizing.

I watched the hustlers in the Port Authority walk their routes like watchmen on inspection, like guards at the Tomb of the Unknown Soldier pacing back and forth martially clacking their shoes, nodding to each other, in the building learning the target spots, the best hours, watching until I could tell the aunties from the paying scores by dress and manner and cruising attitude, and the tourists from the solvent and cockhungry. I thought, you're good-looking, man, you're *handsome*, let's be honest, Angel, you're one thick, dangling, expensive, well hung piece of loving meat. Hot Property. Vitamin packed, Butch, A–Number One Product Nineteen. Without modesty. Like six feet one and dark blond hair, the color of camel's hair or pizza crust, curly, hell! and a hairless chest, big enough, narrowing to the navel, the line, the forest path, the small hair trailing into the pubic zone, darker above Mr. America, thick between my legs under my balls, thick between the cheeks of my ass, my ass unentered and tight, virginal, you better believe it, unsplit as Our Lady of the Little Flower's twat, teacup bottom, rounded, looking in profile like half a cantaloupe on its side, Telling myself I was *better* than okay, building up the courage.

That I thought, but I knew deep in the core of my soul, I *knew* I was kidding myself saying I would not mind the trade, that I would fit, but I did not *like* to be touched by men, I did not appreciate it—and I was not so dumb as to think, outside a male trade service for women, a specialized, incorporated, cake-eater callboy stable, outside of that there was sufficient room to make a life by scoring with broads, not in America, not even in New York City which was the most unAmerican American place I was ever at, not even there would enough broads with enough coins have enough honesty, be straight enough,

47

to pay for the meat when they were bred and raised from the tit to grab and deball and spend the middle years with their thighs gripped tight, their clits atrophying, their minds on the children and the old man's heart and the insurance money and the hope of catching a little free action within the marital limits with the delivery boy; the market was *glutted* with delivery boys believing that a piece of snatch was some gift bestowed, some privilege to be sought and borne as Ganymede bore the golden cup, a privilege hesitantly given when it was and is and forever will be a piece of snatch as wet for you as you are hard for it, maybe—no, I did not like to be touched by men, *friends* perhaps, but *men*, scores, johns, bodies flaccid and uptight with age and bad looks and famished loneliness, without identity, did not like that contrary to what Parker charged. I did not like it, I knew, but was avoiding the knowledge, that the going into trade was going in for other unstated, unrecognized reasons, punishment maybe, hoping to be busted inside, to confront violence necessary and sufficient to make do.

I worked 42nd Street, Third Avenue, the Promenade, even scored in the Ramble and off the meat rack on Central Park West—they waited patient and anxious, finally unembarrassed, standing studiedly casual, bold, in a hopelessly affected Western slouch, waiting to be noticed, waiting ageing, waiting the life narrowing, waiting the hunger becoming rapacious as time dwindled, waiting lined like sick and crippled whores along the stone hedges of the park under the plane trees—learned to hit the tourist bars, the hotels on Broadway and Seventh and Eighth Avenue near Times Square, scored until I had enough. I knew the boys on the street, but lonely, I needed a place. That unambiguous. And I was frightened of ending peddling on the street, like my old man, too late with a product no one wanted anymore. Blind to change.

Then, as summer came, I was saved by boredom and loneliness and, too, really how much can anyone take before the banality of public trade, even with the liberty, gets to be too much, how many times to stand like a bull on meat row in Grand Central and gauge the scores' gaze, decipher which would pay and how much, only so many nights of cruising on 42nd Street, listening to the hustlers in Whelan's Drug Store at the end of the street boast about the take—watching Pete Dannon, from Montana, in his dirty fringed leather jacket and fringed leather pants, roll up his sleeve how many goddamn times to display, at nineteen, an arm marked by knife gougings, suicide incomplete, deep, red culverts jagged up his arm, like teeth on a comb, like the rungs of a ladder, saying he was going to make it right this time, this time going to complete what he had begun—and on my mind remembering Parker walking at night with me on the shore of Lake Michigan rapping about his future. Man, I was missing friends. I decided to find a job, no nine to five crapper but some smooth slot to bring me closer to my friends.

I went looking for a job and a place to live, trying the Village first, no work, the rents impossible, and then making my way into Chelsea, south of Penn Station, near the docks, a dying ghetto. I found a cheap room in a parsonage in the vicinity of General Seminary, tucked under the roof of a belfry on 20th Street—eight dollars a week,

49

at night the pigeons cooed and hovered like raven-sentries on the windowsill, on Sunday the bells.

It was the church's Rector who let the room and hired me, after five minutes of conversation in his kitchen, his wife brewing coffee and laughing at my shyness, the preacher holding his baby in his arms and telling me, as if angels came unawares, that he had a son my age, at West Point, who was growing yearly more distant from the family, more rightwing and elitist. "Just like Peter," he said, laughing, glancing at his wife, "Same color hair, doesn't he have the same color hair though." She shook her head at his enthusiasm, "Not quite," she said.

The Rector had been at the church in Chelsea almost a decade, he had come from the Middle West, from the suburbs of Chicago where I was from, and as he showed me around the church and the parish hall, most of it in disrepair, unpainted, he spoke about his love of Chelsea, the poor, especially the youngsters, "You're going to have to relate to these kids. Help them become men, you're almost there yourself. They need, these boys need the help of the church." He stated that firmly, standing in the nave of the church, the altar before us with its Sunday flowers withered and brown in the brass vases, the small marble tabernacle locked and it, and the silver vessels beside it, washed in a faint red glow, like burnished metal, from the vigil lights above. I next to him, self-conscious in the place not knowing quite how to act, speaking in a whisper in the church as one spoke in whispers in sick rooms and cemeteries.

I was shown my room upstairs, small but possessing a giant window overlooking 20th Street. I put my clothes in the closet, and lay down on the bed and thought about the irony of a hustler ending up in a church teaching boys how to play it straight.

That evening, I had dinner with the family, all of them very nice to me, so kind in fact that I was suspicious of their kindness, openness and easily expressed affection, difficult to believe. We talked about Chicago, the Rector and I hating it, and I told him a bit about Parker and my old man, that scene, and he nodded gravely and described his experiences in the civil rights movement, about the need to enforce the Supreme Court's decisions and build the Brotherhood of Man under the Fatherhood of God. Amen. And then he said, "We make no claim on you, you kids are rolling stones (pastoral sigh), can't hold you down. Peter (his son), raised him to live by the dictates of Christian mercy, and he revolts. We don't ask that anymore. Come to us when you want to, ask what you want. The only rule is that you do what you do fairly. If you have a complaint, tell us. If you want to leave, tell us." Another rulemaker. He excused himself, kissing his wife, and went to say evening prayer at the church.

I helped his wife clear the table and we did the dishes together, she washing, I wiping. Later we made gin and tonics and the three of us, including the baby, went into the living room and she put a Pete Seeger record on. It was a very old Federal house, with French windows which opened onto what had once been a garden but was now a hardened dirt plot. I opened the windows and we sat in the breeze, sipping our drinks, and listening to Seeger sing; the baby cried and the Rector's wife opened her dress and nursed the child at her breast. First time I had seen it done, beautiful thing to see.

Later I went up to my room and sat on the windowsill, as once I had sat on the window seat at my aunt's place, and looked out at the street and the school where I was going to work.

The job I filled was supervising a student pool hall in PS 6. I worked with Irish delinquents and their sisters and two Puerto Rican homosexuals, rejected by their own group, held in asylum with us, paying for integration by doing the crap work, emptying the garbage, cleaning the floors, jogging in the summer heat after sodas they rarely tasted for Irish boys—better looking, better hung, *whiter.* Unhappy kids.

After being in Chelsea for a month, I began to feel very adult, giving orders to kids younger than me by two or three years, I began to feel straight and that feeling was unlike me. I was uncomfortable with it. So I tried to keep my hand in the old life—in *the* life—by doing some occasional hustling, not for the bread necessarily, but for the danger of it, the kick.

On weekends I would go down to the East Village, sometimes up to Harlem or Spanish Harlem, and blow a week's salary on booze, playing it SUCCESS on the weekend. One night I walked home from the Village and I was jumped.

"You motherfuckers!" Billy had me around the neck, his fingers pressed into the front of my throat. Rick punched me hard in the stomach, bringing a night of drinking raging to my chest. And Willie, he stood several feet behind in the entry to PS 6, the knife in his hand trembling.

"I'm sorry." That is what he said, the bastard. His friends released me, dusted me off with elaborate, courtly motions, patted me on the back. A mistake. They never mug their friends, God knows, but how could they tell in the dark with me staggering down 20th Street, my head lowered, wearing a sports jacket, looking like a tourist slumming or like one of the swells from uptown in Chelsea to ride the whores on Eighth Avenue, or one of the seminarians from General working his way home. How could they tell it was me? Street Worker. Feeling phony playing social director to what was left of the Irish Warriors after Freddy and twenty other leaders—half on junk at sixteen, the last mick gang left on Manhattan Island, at that age knowing the taste of violence, of sudden, gentle death—after the first generation was sent to Boys' House never to come back, with the neighborhood turning more Puerto Rican every day and the Village artists moving in for the cheaper rents, the hard pushers behind them, the speed and horse circulating in the community among the young like crisp, sharp booze, tangy, dreamlike, waves of high peddled like gumdrops in the streets; artsy-craftsy, the few lofts gone, renovations begun, displacement, the Chelsea Art Show capping in triumph the new proprietors. Without Freddy the boys kept fucking up the art of mugging. They could not pull off a decent drunk roll without the wino screaming bloody murder and the cops moving in—minutes to flight—or, worse yet, Billy's old lady, the only Protestant on the block, an Orangewoman, coming out with her massive arms flying and brass rings cutting their faces. Grace had escaped their hands. Having screwed up so often they were uptight, *had* to pull it off, and so they did not look close enough and long enough when a potential score moved into the territory, dangling the promise of grass and threads in the hairs of their sight. They jumped too soon too often. Once they bombed a teacher, once an off-duty Anglican priest. Apologies followed. A mistake. Willie holding the knife trembling. I'm sorry. Easy. Willie did not fit. Because he was in point of fact the only real non-loser in the neighborhood—thus in the neighborhood he lost.

"Motherfuckers! Goddamn it, Willie!" Incensed at being jumped, and angry because I liked the boys who did it and angry because they were so careless as to jump *me*. (Or was I flattered by being chosen victim, inadvertently chosen, entering privately into the intimacy of their crime, soft hands on me, bodies thrust against me, hot and damp and trembling, I an object, reduced to that, in the splitting of that moment feeling like Parker acting in the world, equal to him for a second when the thought of my death woke my mind.) The Warriors had stopped thinking when Freddy was taken . . . and for boys playing hood not to think was dangerous.

"The next time you sonsofbitches hit me . . . why the hell don't you see who it is *before* you pull them down? Cocksuckers! You'll end up jumping some plainclothes cop and then you'll really have your butts in a sling." I stood, tense, cooling my head, covering, looking at them huddled together in the doorway, their excitement deflated, embarrassed in being failures in front of me, staring at the ground. Willie rubbing his shirt sleeve against his nose, posing innocent. I was fed up. "No beach tomorrow," I said, taking from them what they spent a week looking toward. "You catch that? And, baby," I said, swinging out my hand and seizing Willie by the hair, his scalp warm and sweaty under my hand, and pulling him toward me, chin up, head back so his eyes looked into my face, "You try it again and I'll drag your ass into the Precinct. That clear?" I, playing closet fuzz, convincing no one, not even myself.

Billy and Rick glanced at me and then looked over at Willie, giving him the cue to soften me up.

"We *said* we was sorry! Man, what you want anyway?" Willie, coming on like a child wrongly punished.

"I want to be able to walk down my street without being hit over the head by three queer punks, that's what." They were not queer and they hated being accused of it, but I think both they and I suspected that there was a relationship between their violence and their manhood.

"Come on," Willie intoned, putting his hand lazily on my arm, freeing all the charm sixteen years had taught him. "I walk you home." He grinned, his voice soft, brushing his hair out of his eyes with his other hand. "So you's safe."

I fell for the line, a sucker for it, flattery by pretended concern, like my old man. Willie did it so well, subtly, the assault carried in the movement of a hand or eye, the tongue wetting his lips, a texture of the voice, a gentleness in manner, almost feminine, contradicted immediately by an awareness of violence festering unreleased beneath his skin. That, the surety of his betrayal of anyone without sufficient motive beyond the sheer kick of betrayal, done because in making betrayal, like making assassination, somehow freedom, in the denial of limits, was made; like

55

that Willie was fated for some dock homicide, a dinge bar knifing, a fall from an overpass. An early, hard death.

"No, you stay." I left and then stopped and looked back. They had returned to their watch in the doorway. "Keep up the good work," I shouted.

On weekends I took the boys and their dates on the IND out to Rockaway Beach. I slept in the sun on a blanket while they played in the water. Occasionally they hustled in the men's room, Willie or Rick standing with their trunks wet and dropped around their sandy feet, scoring off the Puerto Rican twins, lifting a dollar from each for the privilege of going down on mick cock. Uncut.

One Saturday—I was exhausted after a Friday night trying without success to hustle cunt in the Astor and Taft tourist bars, outside the theatre at eleven o'clock, on 59th Street leaning butch, Available, sexy, against the Plaza wall, nothing—and fell asleep as soon as my body hit the warm sand. Late in August. A month until the school year began and my time with them ended. I woke to the sound of wild laughter. A few feet away Willie was standing nude on the blanket, surrounded by girls and boys, some beginning to draw down their suits.

"Christ! Willie, pull up your goddamn trunks!" I saw my job riding on his bare ass, the Port Authority bench waiting, the salesman, CONTRIBUTING TO THE DELINQUENCY OF A MINOR.

"Rosemary's got 'em."

"Rosemary?"

"Yeah. Billy won 'em for her at poker." Ingenuous. Smiling, green eyes. The sun on his skin, his dark hair shaded by it, streaked . . . the sun burning my shoulders, the odor of dead fish and Coppertone . . . Willie loving the commotion like a starlet on her first public promo; Rosemary giggling beside him, her hands cupped in oriental embarrassment over her small mouth. I regretted having made him put on his swim trunks. With the reputation of an easy lover, a bullshit artist, he took pains to practice a smooth kind of flattery on me. Handsome. Lanky. The type of boy who made you think of Huck Finn and other myths about the Tall American before he came of age.

Later that week, late at night, I walked down 20th and found Willie sitting on the stoop in front of his tenement waiting to go inside. They had the first-floor apartment. Most nights Willie was seen there marking time.

"What you doing there so late, Willie? You ought to go in."

He shrugged.

"Come on, Willie, go inside. Some motherfucking cop's going to swing by and pull you in." He sat hunched, his forearms resting on his knees, squeezing a baseball between his hands, alone in the light from the streetlamp.

"No dumb cop aint goin' pull *me* in," he said, looking up at me petulantly, throwing his forelock back with his hand.

I sat down beside him on the stoop. I was nervous. I lit a cigarette and gave it to him and lit another for myself. I waited with him. He was wearing a T-shirt and blue levis and sneakers. It was very hot, the air heavy, no wind. Willie smelled of sweat, but the smell was nice, the smell and the heat from his body next to me. He smoked, saying

57

nothing. He wanted me to leave. I stuck. He would not talk and I wanted to talk for I felt lonely that night, scared because I had one summer to dig in and that summer was nearly gone.

The shades went up in the front room.

"I gotta go, okay?" He stood and flicked his head indicating that I was to leave.

"I'll wait till you get in."

He shrugged. "Serve yourself, man. The old lady's through." And as he went inside the man who had been balling his mother moved out, hat pulled down, coat thrown over his shoulder, middle-aged, well dressed. "Cocksucker," Willie said under his breath as he went inside.

After that when I came home late and saw him sitting in the heat on the stoop waiting for the shade to lift I would take him over to Eighth Avenue and 23rd and buy him Cokes at Nedicks to pass the time.

"Where's your old man?" I asked him once.

"Gone," he said simply, without emotion.

"Gone where?"

"Shit, I guess back to Ireland. I hope he burns in hell." Spoken evenly, coolly.

"How long's he been gone?"

He looked over at me—we were drinking sodas at the counter, the place almost empty—examining me, trying to understand why I wanted to know. I do not think he really trusted me, despite the scrapes I pulled him through (the times I played cover in a store while he lifted from the shelves, the grass and booze procured, the parents on the block I spoke to who were out to break his ass for petty thefts, sons beaten, daughters fingered up), despite my desire to be his friend I was finally not of the area nor the race, not part of the tribe, speaking differently of different things, from a state he could not spell and could not imagine. I had not begun on Chelsea streets. I came from outside, without a known past, older, without a mother gone public whore. "About ten, twelve years ago. I don't know, man. Long time."

"You miss him, Willie?" Again the suspicion in his look. *Men* do not admit to missing other men, not even a father gone.

"Nope."

On the way home I asked him what he wanted out of life.

"I wanna be rich."

"What else?"

"Nothin' else. I wanna be rich and marry a girl like Angie. You know Angie on 23rd?" I nodded that I did. She was second generation Irish. Her father owned a liquor store. "Angie's got the stuff, you know, she's solid. I wanna get me a woman and pull the old lady out of this place and set her up clean. And I wanna pay back the cocksuckers. Man, you come in at night and the dump *smells* like their pricks."

The summer ended in church. The kids who had been part of the project gathered for the service to pay back the church for funding their summer. All together in neat rows in neat clothes, their hair wet and combed flat and straight. Quiet. *Christ have mercy upon us.* Willie, acolyte in white and black waving the censer. Clean behind the smoke. Seemingly younger. I said good-bye. Told them I would see them around. And Rick, acting for the group, gave me a cigarette lighter. Stainless steel. My initials and THE WARRIORS engraved on the front. I moved out. I carried my suitcase along 20th Street and waved at them playing stickball in the street.

In about a month I had me a chick who went to N.Y.U. She was out to make me respectable. And like I *wanted* to be housebroken, clean and quiet, with the television and the papa chair and the plugging in on Duty. I did not want to spend my life hustling after what with what, some fucking dreams that came nearer but never within reach if you, like my old man, peddled so many thousands of diplomas or sermons or pieces of ass.

I got a job as a clerk in a bank. I took an apartment on Bedford Street, off Christopher, fifth floor walkup. I gave it all I got, even worked at thinking respectable: good clothes, things to own, going to college, more things, working my way up the System, even more things, and finding safety and a name and that most American Easy Street, living-on-credit. Willie I forgot. And Chelsea hustling and how easily a sale is made, how easily forgotten. For a time.

During the first week of November I went in a taxi down Ninth Avenue and had it pause at the corner of 20th, by General Seminary. I looked down the street, the stoops empty in the chill, school over for the day, the whores beginning to pace out along the avenue at dusk ... the boys playing stickball under the shadow of the bell tower, Spanish music coming from the tenements, junkies new and plain. And for a moment I wondered if the Warriors would hide huddled against the brick of PS 6 that night and drop out of the darkness on some slumming swell from uptown. I saw Willie and called out and waved as the taxi moved away. I missed the street. Freedom there.

Around Thanksgiving, Willie phoned and came up and I gave him a drink which he did not drink and we tried to talk but it was hard to do. The furniture, what there was of it, intimidated him, and I intimidated him, pouring drinks. And he, damn him, just by being there made the straight scene seem phony and anti-life. And I seemed phony in that room.

"Sweet life, man, lot different from the neighborhood," he said, after he dropped the news that he had not gone back to school and Billy was off again to Rikers Island for a year. Pushing. Claimed the police planted the grass. I believed him.

"Where you cop that?" he asked, pointing to the television, walking around the room like a buyer, not quite approving the pad. I felt uncomfortable with him slipping around. I think I was ashamed of the crap in the apartment, of the apartment itself, like he had said I was trying to sell out, and laughing because he knew that I knew there was no buyer in sight.

"Macy's. On credit." I mentioned the credit bit so he would not think I had money and hit me for some coins. "It isn't paid for . . . nor is that either," I said, as he indicated the record player.

He lit a cigarette and sat down on one of my two overstuffed chairs, slouching into the cushion, his green eyes shining from the lamp light and smoke, wearing denim pants and a sweater and no coat. Envy, I thought, or disgust quieted him. I told him about my chick and about my future, neat, buying me. He was as indifferent to my future as to his own. The future only acted to indict. It was a drag.

"How's it going with you, Willie?"

"Okay. Out of bread but that aint unusual. It's okay."

That was all there was. The conversation died. I stood up, he took the hint and rose and I led him to the door. There he stopped, the door partially open, and looked at me as if he wanted to say something, then shook his head as if he had decided not to and then started out.

"What did you want to say, kid?" I asked, grabbing his arm.

"Nothin'. Just . . ."

He leaned against the door frame, his face outlined against the hall light, eyes lowered. "When do you . . . what time you get in from work?"

"Why?" Suspicious.

"I thought . . . well, I thought I might stay some night, you know, when . . ."

"Haven't you any place to stay?"

He was offended. "What you *mean*, no place, man? I got the old lady's place. You stupid or somethin'?"

"Just asked."

"Stupid, that aint what I meant."

Two days later FAGGOT was scrawled over the walls, the chairs had been pissed on, the television, phonograph, my clothes, everything of value taken. What was not taken was destroyed. Willie. That son of a bitch. Seeing the damage, sitting on the floor looking at the damage, the smell of urine—*his* piss—coming from the fucking chairs, thinking of Willie I missed the bastard and, in a sense, loved him. It was not the goddamn furniture nor the theft which bothered me, it was the FAGGOT slashed across the walls. Damn punk knew about the hustling. Big deal. HUSTLERS ARE NOT QUEER. Didn't he *know* that? Me, I was no miss mary pansy. I never let a score touch me, never, just the mouth and meat, no more, and Willie thought I was some kind of fairy getting a thrill out of being done. It was *business*. It was that, the suspicion that he suspected what I could not, what I did not suspect, that he suspected it and threw it at me like Truth when it was no truth, or the chance of it being truth was small, too small to count. God, we have to pay. It comes down to paying the rent, and how you do it, if you do it by the rules, doesn't make any difference. But that FAGGOT thing, that was not fair. No, not at all, not from a friend.

And he wanted to stay the night. I remember. HUSTLERS ARE NOT QUEER. That he, Willie, should remember like a friend. That he should not forget.

I called my girl and moved in with her that night and lay awake thinking of how to make the little mick pay. I wanted to hurt him, didn't he hurt me? Not so much for what he had done—I knew already in a way with the destruction he had done me one big favor for it ended then the playing respectable shit, no more building nests with N.Y.U. broads and thinking about degrees and the rest of that straight bullshit, no more this being bribed by

the Westinghouse-General Electric-Mother Bell future—
what he had done in cutting up and destroying was a
pretext to hit him, but because he was weaker than me
and hopeless and sticky with his very own death coming
his way, and I was fond of him and that was dangerous
and when he wrote his big straight word on the wall
he sold out, he broke the rule, Parker's thing about
loyalty, he betrayed. And I had to remake the balance,
even though I *wanted* him to betray, hoping for something worse. And that was what he offered, an insult, that
and in his body, when he came around, the sense of
violence, like an anointment, like the odor of defeat, more
there than any future. Sensual. It freed me. What he had
done was liberating and it was cheap. Without adequate
cause. I wanted to hit him lower, to balance things.

Monday night. I remember it well because the weather
was unseasonably warm for late November and rain was
predicted and I carried an umbrella as I walked up Eighth
Avenue from the Village and over to 20th and I waved the
umbrella at Rick and smiled at him and he ran over and
said, grinning, happy to see me, "Wait 'til I find Willie.
Stay here, man, I'll be right back!" and I carried the umbrella up the steps and into the hall and knocked on the
door with it and handed it to Willie's mother and said
nothing, simply walked into the apartment and threw
thirty dollars on the sofa; she nodded and pointed at the
bedroom and left me, going into the bathroom; and I did
not take off my clothes but walked around enjoying the
apartment, my trousers undone, wandered into Willie's
room and looked at the picture of his mother, younger

then, with his old man, who looked like Willie, standing in a brass frame on the bureau, and I took out the cigarette lighter with my initials and THE WARRIORS engraved on the front and dropped it on his bed; the toilet flushed; I moved back into the bedroom and flopped down on the big bed and his old lady came in, makeup on, her lipstick spread heavily, wide of the mark like in a forties movie, and I pointed at my cock and she shook her head No, I tossed twenty dollars more on the bed and like a hustler I lay back as she went down on me. I thought of Willie.

chapter six

A YEAR later, in the early fall, I saw Willie standing by
the newspaper stand at 42nd Street and Broadway, the
rain coming down and catching the neon light, millions
of colored bits of polished crystal raining curtainlike before
the awning under which Willie stood in a leather jacket
and jeans and boots, his hair long, his appearance and
his mannered hustlerlike slouch; time-to-kill, I thought.
Available, I thought, with the rain coming and the water
spraying masses of pink color under the traffic against
the curb, the color gripped by the water like Buckingham
Fountain at night when the lights are on it in the summertime and the lights in the distance across Grant Park
from the Chicago skyline walled at Michigan Avenue and
beyond reflected, too, in the breaking water. I was on the
other side of the street, under the canopy of the cigar
store. I recognized Willie, but I could not determine his
expression and his mood (and I could not see his green
eyes, and I was lonely for his green eyes, for the green
of his eyes; that happens, you know, loneliness for a
particular color in a specific place) because of the crowds,

the umbrellas, the rain, the modifying, concealing light. And I thought of the docks because of his wet and shiny jacket, the leather bars jammed that night, the air musty with the smell of leather damp from the rain, sawdust on the floor, together the odors reminding one of stables and horses, maleness, enormous peckers promised by the created, almost cosmetic mounds at the crotch, nowhere bars devoid of payoff queens, scores, devoid of commerce. The violence latent and unrealized in the strutting leather jackets, in the smell, the phony toughs sweating in the leather in the jammed bar but unwilling to take the jacket off for that was, the jacket, all *they* were, what they respected and lusted and spent days working for, selling ribbons at Saks, designing sets and silks and furniture groupings, styling the brittle, baked-out hair of yentas, mail boys, clerks, junior editors, waiters, second rate actors, journalists, working the week to escape into themselves—captured magically, mnemonically in smooth-grained hide.

Willie, and to my mind the sight of him crowding under the awning on the street, and my ineffaceable, incontinent guilt, not over the act of fucking his mother, over the *motive* for the act (disgruntled love) and thinking that the boy is probably playing pocket pool, his hand in his jeans gripping his balls and thinking the many handsome ways to fold out into nothingness; peace; waiting for him was that goddamn angel smiling and marking time to taste his blood, the angel that loves this America so much. That I was thinking, standing across the street looking at Willie, I was thinking he aint one of the survivors, not old Willie.

To avoid him, because I wanted to run through the rain

67

and slip up to Willie boy, Willie seventeen and untough despite the try, my cowboy, lonesome in the rain . . . and when you do the street you think a lot about being a cowboy and about riding the goddamn range with Big John Wayne on a horse and sleeping on a blanket with your buddies by a guttering fire with the sky above unblighted by Con Edison light and the muscles tired from honest work, and the sweat honest, and the stink honest, and even the lonesomeness honest because it is kind of pure being it comes from the Plains, from America untouched and unpolluted, its murders on the range clean for being apolitical, done in nobody's name, for no damn cause or abstraction, being personal about immediate things, human things, like horse thefts and gold digger saloon brawls and dancing women. So that is the myth that makes the street boy Romantic and American and makes him—at this distance—touching, for it makes you able to deny the real cause of estrangement in your youth in your city which never has nor will belong to you, able to negate and dismiss it by laying hands on the John Wayne/Wild Bill Hickock/Jesse James America that really exists out there somewhere, I guess, where real cowboys ride horses and herd cows along the plains where real Indians lurk in the Badlands and draw smoke signals against the sky and, knowing that, it makes the body adopt a home it never saw—the West—as its place to miss . . . to avoid Willie The Cowboy, hoping he was not part of the street scene, not wanting to confront him—not because of guilt, the hesitancy, but love again and the inability to explain to him my life, with me standing in cruddy jeans and a torn shirt and a real frontiersman rust-colored suede jacket with the

68

long Wild West rawhide fringes on the sleeves and tooled cowboy boots on my feet— I walked down 42nd Street to the Dixie Hotel, keeping my face angled toward the wall away from him, and sat in the tacky, dark lobby for an hour. When I hit the street again, Willie was gone.

chapter seven

THAT evening, after catching sight of Willie, I tried to score in a few bars but something had gone out of the city or out of me, and there were gray and empty spaces left, like the drafty passages between old buildings—that, and the rain.

Hustlers are not queer. That I knew. Even when I stood with my legs spread, with the meat, my meat, being lapped by a john, I was not gay, for my mind—my *unminty* imagination—was scouting past the mouthworker to other things. Maybe the weather, or dinner missed, or what I would do with the ten bills being earned there from the size queen or, near the end, maybe thinking of Willie. But *non*sexually, you understand. If it was sexual, I could not have admitted it.

I loved Willie, like a brother I loved him. And I was afraid of seeing him after using his old lady like you use a man. I was afraid he knew, and knowing it he hated me. And yet, contradiction, I *wanted* him to know. For that was the point of it all. To hurt him because I loved him and he had cheated that love by charging falsely that I was a faggot, a faggot for him, when I was no faggot. So I avoided him until I saw him in the rain. And even then I was afraid to be seen by him. I missed him, watching him, I missed the kid.

When I came out of the Dixie Hotel and found him gone I grabbed a train down to the Village, and wandered around in the wet streets for a time. Finally, I went over to Houston Street, near Little Italy, to a restaurant where Coretta worked nights as hostess.

I had met Coretta when I first came to New York. Sometime during the first few weeks I had gone to the 19th Street Bar, walked in and shoved my ass down through the crowd of men to the back room—cold outside, the bar overheated and smelling like gym shoes—where I spotted her, her face patterned by the light banging red and blue against a turning mirrored ball. Typical cruise saloon: hustlers, closet queens, voyeurs, two-way men, aunties, basketeers, floaters, the American Male unresplendent after the wars and womanhood rising triumphant, deballing the nation. And Coretta sat in the back room like a queen trying to maintain majestic decorum in a palace fallen to the carousing mob, muffled in perfumes, the only lady in the joint, and I was horny for pussy that night (as if I had to tie in with a chick to make myself true) feeling unsure of my manhood with my stomach still quivering like a loverboy's after seeing Willie but briefly. Noticing the broad, I went over to Coretta's table, on the make. I moved in beside her and looked at her close. Something odd.

What everyone first saw and what they remembered about Coretta was her size, not only her shoulders, which were immense, Samsonesque, but her fullback's thighs and calves, and butcher's hands. And her thick, mannish neck. Under the powder her neck was barn red, like a plow-boy's. To see her move then with that recent, impossible delicacy, her skin painted membrane-white, like a china doll's, her hands held high and out, angled precisely, like wings unfolded, fluttering to her mouth to cover her buck teeth and manly laugh, a snort . . . her feet mincing tiny, lilting steps, one foot close to the next, walking along as if the path were three inches wide and balancing were extremely difficult. The collapse of femininity: the manner in which she daintily tugged her skirt down, smoothing her backside, crossing her legs properly, her hands flutter-ing—mothlike—concern over her hair. Coretta, parody, cunt and all, but a parody of what she longed to gift men with: her very own, prepaid, functioning little box.

I remember that night very well since I had come to the 19th Street Bar torn up inside after witnessing a black queen, in red tennis shoes and blouse and lounge pants, and a white hustler she loved, in denim and boots, no shirt in the cold, run in the blowing sleet across Eighth Avenue at 22nd Street, and the hustler she loved being hit by a fast blue-paneled truck, hit and flying high, crashing ten feet against the curbside, his face skidding off in blood along the wet asphalt. The queen screaming like Rachel mourning uncomforted her slaughtered children, disconso-late, screeching hysterically like some frantic, wild and fearsome desert bird and throwing her hands to her face and sobbing, passing back and forth in the street and collecting the books the hustler she loved had carried, weeping, conveying them like caskets of myrrh to his body in her queenly arms majestically and wailing until the sheet was dropped like night over him and he was taken. In the 19th Street Bar I went up and sat at Coretta's table and smiled at her, played the hick, and she smiled in return, and gradually moved her body in profile so I could gaze at her arching breasts. I told her about the hustler smashed like glass across the pavement and of the hysterical queen. "Oh, God!" she groaned, "Don't ever let me be that hung on a man!"

I drank at the booth in the front room of the restaurant, near the door, where I could watch Coretta. We had become friends of sorts, running into each other on the street, especially in the Village, having friends in common. Sometimes at night, generally when I was emotionally down or out of bread, I would come into the restaurant and play her Gentleman Caller, as I did that night, when closing time was approaching and the patrons were thinning out, only a few tourists wandering in late to catch one for the road as they sat and leered.

Coretta ... I watched her work, thinking that both she and Willie, and yes, Parker and Doris and how many others were fugitives and victims. The best of the crowd in the heart to me, but losers each for different, equally sad reasons, Willie's being his love of the promise of violence and his need, as a hustler, to be pursued.

It aint easy, I thought, being her kind of woman, to try goddamn hard how many nights to walk a real lady-walk through the waterfront bars and Jersey City bars and other narrow places where she went to find workmen on her nights off—workers with their paychecks cashed, feeling stud, shirts stain fermented, bonetired, aching to take the foreman's anger out on some real lady-walking bitch, not wanting to go home yet to face their old ladies and their kids . . . workmen drinking Rheingold beer in dusty corner bars and cruising in the bad air and staring astonished, rubbing the front of their trousers and elbowing their pals as Coretta walked her real lady-walk through the thin passages past their groping hands, her eyes looking neither left nor right, thinking of how Jane Russell used to swing her tits and butt before she went fat and Christian, trying to pull it off authentically *femme* . . . praying, Dear God, that they go for her tight ass, feeling up her dress, saying nothing, her head thrust regally in the air, a self-regarding Lana-Turner smile on her face, letting them grope. Man, to feel their strong hands grope.

Two middle-aged men came into the restaurant, obvious fags looking too groomed and too piss-elegant. She led them into the front room, swinging her ass hopefully as she walked, winking at me as she passed with her troupe in hand, like a stern teacher herding two truants into school, dignity, the two queens cruising me, and I staring back, scratching my belly as they went by, and I thought, watching her do her stuff, it aint easy being her kind of woman and surviving under the paint and Dynel hair, the soul intact enough to keep the lungs filled with hope (and for some reason I remembered auntie's line about the family being not a thing of the blood, her bullshit about friends. I wondered if I held Coretta to me as a friend, if I had come that far to meet her equally) bending over now and the thrill of the sensation of new breasts hanging free like her cock must once have dangled before the trip to Baltimore and the cutting.

74

It couldn't be easy to chance the light, being her, to hide football-rough hands under gloves, to beg off with claims of periods unexperienced, to place faith in hormone pills and silicone shots and the most unconvincing of unconvincing snatches. The Ultimate Technetronic Queen. The most real of the fake American Beauties. Miss Mary Miserable martyred, self-beatified, elevated, god-whore personified when she saw herself in virgin white, pursuing where she begged pursuit, shaking her ass in every male face and hoping it does not look too close, ask too much ... *just drain in me, just do that for me, forget the love shit, okay? I need it but forget it. Just pump it in like it's boyass. And with pretense I'll make do.* . . . "God, I need a *man!*" she said to Rodney, he the first to get her when she returned from Johns Hopkins recreated and covenanted, and was hung on Teddy Kennedy, bad back and all. She wanted to be balled by him. PATRIOTIC DUTY, Miss Liberty. Upend me, Ted. And she was a Republican to boot.

Coretta came over to my table and seated herself in what she considered a seductive manner. "My feet are *killing* me. Oh, my," she sighed, smiling at me, "what I wouldn't give for someone's . . . some *stud's* cold back to rest my tootsies against." She flagged the busboy and asked for a Coke. "Lots of ice and lemon." He brought it and she swatted his ass as he left, the way NLF players pat each other's bottoms off the field. "Cute kid, no?" she asked, her mind on other things. "I saw this film, see," she said, going into what was on her mind, "where Marilyn Monroe climbs into a train compartment with Jack Lemmon, and he's in drag, and they're rolling around in the

75

bunk, all those girls and Marilyn and Lemmon, hoping the conductor don't catch them, sexy . . . *mary!* like bitches on a stick . . . and I wanted to *be* Marilyn Monroe, or like her anyway, those big titties."

She went on rambling, and I knew she was getting me to dig her transfigurement: "I saw those stag films, too. You weren't around then, but that cocksucker Rodney, you remember him?" (I remember him painting on the Lower East Side, moody. Undiscovered Genius, and, later, in West Harlem near Columbia University, young, dark, goodlooking like an English schoolboy, the white, porcelain skin, aristocratic blue veins, like wispy pencil lines, at the side of his forehead, claiming he was the founder of a revolutionary school of art—*Pubism*, he called it—his masterpiece being a gigantic portrait of George Washington posing on the boat crossing the Delaware and sporting a massive black penis. And Rodney made a plastic cast of the imprint of a twat which he entered in a straight East Side show and called MOTHER [the explicit taken as abstract, it won a prize], "Rodney took me to those dirty pictures, it was at a party on Mulberry Street, always had me dress in a sailor suit and sing 'Anchors Aweigh' and they had this film, *A Nun's Story* or something like that, where a bandit comes in wearing a black mask like the Lone Ranger and fucks and fingers and fucks again this nun, who just eats it up like so much candy, his prick sticking out of his underpants like a sail in the wind . . . I wanted to be that nun."

Coretta took another sip of her Coke, glancing at me shyly above the top of her glass, talking softly. It was about 2 A.M. and she was through for the night, the door open and the air coming in cool and clean, the smell of the Hudson filtering in, her feet killing her from working all night as hostess, showing tables to the tourists, smiling at the men, letting them touch her when their wives were not looking, handing them menus, giving out the Lana-Turner smile, the sad smile, the hooker's wink, the longing-helpless-cunning-feminine need spread on her tongue with the saliva on her lips, half-opened, taking a discreetly given, discreetly received dollar bill slipped into her palm, shoving it into the expensive cleavage of her breasts while the male tourist looked on and counted the years. Mama, there's nobody like Coretta in Akron. Nobody as devoutly feminine and as piously submissive to the male will, as contrite in the worship of the American phallus. A nun. Bride of Christ, eternally in waiting for the bridegroom ... her lamps kept oiled, the wicks trimmed, seeing his coming always as a thief in the night, prepared that at any hour the shout may rend the heavens: the Bridegroom cometh! Until then, the tourist from Akron, his smell lacquered over by Old Spice. But never as nice as it was with Marilyn. Never as clean.

"This nun was never fucked before. Wasn't used to it. He finger-fucked her nest. Shit, I got all moist watching that Lone Ranger slip his fingers up her snatch, got the chair wet just watching. It was so beautiful, him all hard and still with his curtains." Coretta paused, savoring it, recalling the DREAM, purchased, cheaper than some, with a surgeon's knife, balled now as she balled before, in another man's cock finding a reflection of her own and through it possessing herself—past self, the prize, pulling up the straps of her dress, shaking her breasts a trifle as she did, glancing up at me and gauging the effect of the gesture and the tale. "He stands up ... he comes, see ... and his thing's going soft and this nun pulls herself up and takes his prick ... been *inside* her, for Christ's sake! and sucks it ... a *nun* sucking a *cock*. Lord Almighty!" Coretta squealed, wrapping her big arms around herself, sounding as if she were about to levitate. "So beautiful. Wouldn't it of been wonderful to of been that sister?"

I walked her home from the restaurant, her feet aching and her face looking tired, and as usual people on the street did double takes. We went down Saint Marks Place, about a block past the Electric Circus, to her pad, past the hippies panhandling late on the street, the dinge toughs grouped on the stoops, Coretta leaned on my arm, the tired queen, virgin mother, and I thought this was no place for a lady, not with the flower children gone early, the toughs and bikeboys and losers left on the edges of Tompkins Park and on the streets breeding violence, this was no place for a lady, and even though Coretta could knock the hell out of anyone on the street, being a lady she would not.

As we walked, I became more depressed, wondering what the hell I was doing strolling home with Mary Miserable when it was sex which was on her mind, and my mind was free of it, unless it was sublimated into Willie's form so profoundly that in grooving on him—I was still stoned on the inadvertent sight of Willieboy standing under the Times Square awning in the rain—I was grooving sexually. And that idea nearly stopped me in my tracks, like I maybe wanted sex with Coretta, wanted it but would not admit to myself that I wanted it,

78

because with her I could make it with a boy and call it a girlfuck and escape without the hangover/guilt. Did not require Willie's old lady (and even then in my imagination in making her slip her tongue over my tool, in that it was a man's act. Like women you screwed, *men* went down on you. And as she sucked, yes, it was Willie on my mind) anymore to make it vicariously with Willie. I was growing more subtle. Just ball a girl/former boy and, in the residue of Coretta's manhood, I would be embracing Willie. Now that is probably what I thought *after* fucking Coretta, but it seemed I must have considered it before I reached her place. I was not dumb.

Up four flights, she walking barefoot. She found high heels difficult to manage on the stairs. Inside her room. Girl dolls on the bed. A vanity table with a chintz frill around its base. Everywhere cologne, dresses, bras, stockings, panties, high-heel shoes, some with ankle straps like in forties movies. And the pathetic insistence on the ultimate burlesque: that I wear a rubber to protect her dead hole from babymaking. I crawled into bed, unerect, turned off, as she undressed modestly in the dark. Acquired modesty.

When I saw her moving toward me in the darkness, the heavy imbalanced breasts shaking with her walk, the large thighs, careful not to turn her back and expose to me a profile more rugged than my own, when I saw her huge man's body princessing toward me and sighing into bed beside me, what turned me on was the picture of that vastly endowed man/woman costumed in thinly tapered, high spiked boots tight around her calves and a leather belt, like cowboys wear, strapped across her chest like a

79

warrior's girdle, her breasts bulging over it, and a six-shooter in her hand (Willie the Cowboy).

She lay next to me on the bed, breathing fast, lying on her back with her breasts rising and falling, appearing foreign to her body, imposed, large lumps like sand-filled bags on her chest. What had it cost her to lie there by me, the cutting and the pain and the anguish unrelieved and mounting shame and past forbidden and condemned and memory shut out like an orphaned child. To pay so dearly to become other than she was born to be. To sacrifice and scale the hill and bend backward beneath the cutting edge and searing lights and to lurch beyond the point of no return. To return transfigured into herself. God, it did not work. Her kind of woman, and still she could not pull it off. Without escape.

"Why you so quiet tonight?" she asked, nudging me with her hand, moving it lazily across my chest, playing with my nipples, making them hard.

"I feel lonesome."

"For what?" Moving her hand wide over my stomach, gently tugging at the small hairs below my navel.

"For a kid. A friend. I don't know. For lots of things."

"I get lonesome, too," she said, laying her head on my shoulder, her oversprayed hair like straw against my cheek. "I knew a boy in Texas. I was in the Air Force there. . . . It gets so goddamn *hot* in Texas. It's so flat, the land is," the weather and the contours of the earth an afterthought, and I could dimly see her body in the window light, aging as a man's body ages, going flaccid in the stomach, the butt and belly and thighs rebounding to the touch, the belly hanging as a man's belly hangs as it ages, ". . . I hated Texas, but I miss it. You miss any place?"

I thought a moment. Evanston. Missed it in a way, as it was when I was a kid. No, I did not miss Evanston now. What I missed, what I was lonesome for, was the people, a myth about people, about friends I used to know there. Like there were friends out there in America for me who in some crazy way I had betrayed or disowned and lost or never discovered, but who I was accountable to. That imprecise. "No, I miss no place."

"I sorta miss Texas. There was this lieutenant named Cortney who I was in love with there . . . one night he drove me back to the base and I leaned over and gave him a kiss . . . because I loved him so goddamn much, and this here cocksucking M.P. sees and blabs. We both got court-martialed. Cort and me. A real mess."

"I didn't know you were in the Air Force. I really didn't know."

She laughed, and stretched her hand flat on the base of my stomach and pushed it in little jerks down to my groin, to the base of my penis, and with her thumb and forefinger, as she spoke, almost absentmindedly, circled the root of my sex with her fingers, like a wedding band, and pulled the skin back and forth, casually, as it grew stiff. "Yes, I was in with the fliers. Ha! But even in Texas I *knew* I had a woman's heart, loving the stronger sex as I do." Here she tugged at my penis, flipping it back against my stomach. "And in this fucking country you got to be either a man or a woman, that's all there is, pet, so, well . . . I was never *really* a man. I was a virgin. Never fucked nothing except my hand, and I liked to get buttfucked.

81

But, shit, you can't spend your *life* getting arrested by squares for sodomy like you're some kind of whore...."
Then, considering me, "Not that it's *wrong* to be a whore, lot of whores and hustlers are great, but I wanted a house and a family and I wanted to marry some good man and make his breakfast and dinner, you know, and do the housework for him, like an honest wife. I wanted to be happy and live in a country house somewhere, a house with everything on the same floor. Oh, I wanted to be happy. I got a *right* to be happy, that's in the Constitution! So I thought, I got to become *me*, a lady, you can't arrest a *lady* for getting balled by a stud, now can you?" The logic of it all. "But you know," she said, regret coming like the Horseman in the end, paling, the angel thieving already before the kiss, "it don't work out that way. I think ... shit! Sometimes I think it was an awful mistake, the operation."

She was silent for a time. She moved her head down my belly and licked my groin and penis. I pulled her back up to my chest. I was in no mood for a head job. Who needs it? Could leave and get ten bucks being done uptown. If she were a lady, then ladies screwed.

"Hell, the men that ball me ... I don't mean you, honey," she said, meaning me, "well they ... I think they're fags." She said "fags" bitchily. "Real tough! Shit. *Too* goddamn tough! A lot of army men, most I guess. They can't own up to wanting some man, somebody their eyes fix on in their unit or something, and they follow him at parades and take showers to get a peek at his meat or ass, you know, and I'm not quite a man to *them*, but I have a cunt ... *I really have a cunt!* Like any other girl! They want to fuck their buddy and they think in their sick heads that it's really okay to fuck a boy as long as it's me because I am really a girl, legally. So they get what they want. Boyass."

She stopped talking and rubbed the sleep out of her eyes, exhausted, her hand smearing the mascara on her eyelids. "Those bastards! They fuck me in the ass as if my snatch wasn't even there, for Christ's sake! It aint fair! Goddamn it! Perverts. A pack of frigging perverts, that's what American men are. . . . Oh, God, *dear* God, I never should've done that operation, never . . . I want to die, baby, only to die."

I touched her head and caressed her cheek. Time passed. I lay there thinking more and more about doing what she hated, buttfucking her just like she was nothing but a man. "Coretta, what about maybe . . . what you say maybe putting on some shoes and gloves or something and doing it out of bed? Like against the wall? What you say, baby?" I knew she was in the mood to make love, *romantic* love. I wanted to keep it sexual by keeping it a boy-rape fantasy in my head so I could keep *it* up. It was beyond me, the ability to take that hole seriously, the front one.

Her reply, sad, broken, making me feel like an all-around bastard, "You're all mean . . . all you men are cruel, cruel to us girls." Whimpering, that big woman lay sprawled at my side, bigger than me, for God's sake, and I tried to wield my imagination into order to screw, thinking of the black queen gone hysteric and the dead hustler she loved in the street. Hopeless, for my mind, incontinent, kept brooding on Willie. And I rolled her over on her stomach, with her crying, and kept her there and moved my fingers over her ass and then spread it cuntwide and shoved Mister America up her butt. She could've been a score.

Later she started to cry again. For no reason clear to me, to cry as a man cries, low, wailing tones, and I reached over and put my arms around her broad body, took her tight in my arms, pulled her to me and caressed her head, the black roots an inch high, the blonde pale and phony, un-Marilyn Monroe. We fell asleep with me holding him in my arms like a small boy. Like Willie. Gently.

chapter eight

WHEN I pushed on the street again, after Chelsea and after leaving my chick on Bedford Street (I was not fixed to live inside nine-to-five) I stayed in a series of fleabag hotels in the Forties between Eighth and Ninth Avenues, places like the Elysian Arms, the Kensington Palace, and the last dump I lived in, the Pacific Moon Hotel. Each had a bare lobby with a booth at the end surmounted by a metal screen. Behind the screen sat an old lady who took a week's rent in advance and bitched about my using too many towels.

The hotels were eight or ten stories tall, with automatic elevators which seldom worked and which smelled, like the corners of the halls, of urine; green or yellow-white painted walls, bare bulbs, low wattage, and old flypaper curling from the ceilings, from fantastically ornately molded ceilings catching and holding shadows; floors without rugs, peeled linoleum, and, always, like in tombs and railroad tunnels, echoes. (In South Chicago, was it behind the yards? there was an abandoned railroad tunnel where Doris and Parker once went with me, and we smoked grass and Parker and I pissed looking at each other laughing, and the sound of our water hitting the concrete resounded, enlarged in echo, like an elegant, princely fountain, like the fountains built in Grant Park with the slaughterhouse fortunes.) All night echoing human voices, argument, Spanish laughter, old men's wailing muted like a trumpet.

No one talked in the corridors of the hotels. Not once, not to me.

In the afternoons I came out of my room into the hall and it was dark like nighttime and I often saw someone padding down the corridor, a middle aged man in underpants headed toward the bathroom or some old broad in curlers and flannel robe and bunny slippers peeking out of her room, catching sight of me and jerking herself back inside, slamming the door. It offended me when doors were slammed. People hulking through the halls quietly. It scared me, like a presentiment of a sinister future. That was how I suspected I would end. I dreaded it. People old, and smelling of bad booze and cheap, medicated soap. I used to think it would be better to commit a sensational murder at sixty, an assassination maybe, than to die obscure.

I was never in a loony bin, however the Pacific Moon will do. Old folks shuffling about speechless, and at night noises loud, but at great distance.

There was a framed Salvation Army poster at the Pacific Moon, printed in the 1940s, which I liked because the Army lassie on it was pretty and very passive, reminding me of rural girls in school picture books. She had nothing whatever to do with the caption on the poster: THE

WAGES OF SIN IS DEATH. CHRIST DIED FOR YOUR SINS. The Salvation Army shield, and *Blood and Fire* printed under it. Blood and fire. Blood and sperm.

Some nights—the meetings were held on Wednesdays through Saturdays—I went over to the Salvation Army storefront church off Broadway. They had a five piece band, a lot of bellowing drunks, lassies with tamborines, and free sandwiches after the Altar Call. *Are your garments spotless, are they white as snow, are you washed in the blood of the Lamb?*

For three nights in a row a man waited for me outside the storefront church. I sat on a wooden folding chair near the plate glass window. I saw him standing smoking near the doorway. He was in his thirties, with a crewcut, suited, with a bow tie like academics affected in the fifties. He was nice-looking, or rather he was strong-looking, with a face you could cast as one of Scott Fitzgerald's heroes returning home a decade after high school to run alone in the late afternoon down the hometown football field toward the goalposts remembering the winning touchdown. His name was Cooper, as in Gary Cooper. He taught History at Yale University. He was married, had a little baby boy, and lived outside of New Haven. His wife, whom I never met, was frigid or something, anyway she had trouble with her periods and complained of mysterious discharges from her hole which took her periodically to Indiana to her mother.

Cooper was similar to a lot of johns, the clean type, the ones you could never figure out why they paid for it, why they did not hit the gay bars downtown rather than hang around Grand Central or the Third Avenue cafes after

87

five, before nine, hang around nervously looking at their watches, computing the time to the next, the last commuter train to Connecticut. But payment had something to do with the need for humiliation, for contrived shame, and for control. As long as you paid you weren't a fag. Conversely, as long as you were bought, too, you were not one either. It was, psychologically, a safe bet.

Cooper was the only score I ever brought to my room at the Pacific Moon Hotel. The fifth night, outside the Salvation Army, he stopped me, after four nights of ambiguous cruising, got up the nerve. "Are you in school?" The guy was an amateur.

First we went up to the Yale Club, to the bar upstairs (I did not like the place, the people suspicious—and it was not warm inside, the temperature. I shivered). I looked too much like a hustler and it unnerved Cooper, and he got embarrassed and fumbled around ordering the drinks, referring to me loudly as Mister Smith, which wasn't my name, and when a friend of his came into the bar, he said, "Jack, I want you to meet John Smith," indicating me, "former student of mine. Art History major, wasn't that it, Mister Smith?" and his friend looked at the two of us knowingly, that is, censurously, and Cooper and I made a hasty exit leaving our drinks undrunk behind. Altogether a bad show.

We went to another bar, some tourist trap on Broadway, and he started rambling about his kid and his wife, sitting across from me chain smoking, not at his ease, talking quickly trying to fill in the space with words until our drinks were downed, for he felt clumsy, not quite knowing how to go about it, seduction, not understanding that

88

the bread was the seduction and a hustler was not a seventeen-year-old first date you had to impress with good character. "I did not want a baby. Marge, that's my loving wife, she wanted it. The bitch. Really can't afford to have a child. It's a lousy world to bring up a boy in anyway. For her mother, I guess, to certify my manhood. Although Marge has never said anything, still, sometimes I think maybe . . . God, would she die if she knew about you." He laughed. The man was afraid of his wife. "Do you plan on having any kids?"

He was serious and I was taken back, I had never been asked that by anyone, never really thought about it much. "I don't know. Sometime." I had not made up my mind.

"Well, don't," he said, "All they do is grow up and hate you. Give my kid fifteen years or less. He'll hate both Marge and me. Kids are honest. Nothing escapes them."

All the time I knew Cooper he persisted in doing two things. Shoving five-dollar bills in my pants pockets on the street, and trying to feel me up in the process. And he kept correcting my grammar. He was the first person to tell me it was not correct to say "Between you and I." Told me how to use "whom" and that there was no such word as "irregardless." And he also said that you never begin a sentence with "and" or end it with a participle dangling, no matter what for.

The first night was pretty bad. The Pacific Moon intimidated him. The lady in the cage demanded five bucks to let him use my room. She was no dummy.

When we got upstairs he did not want to make it, not at first, instead he sat around talking about books, poetry, writers, and about what a lousy poet James Dickey was. I had never heard of the man.

"I thought a dickey was something you wore," that's me playing coy.

"No, it's something you suck."

With that the Yale prof went down on me, yet he had no erection, and later I had to stand in the room with my legs spread, my hand on my waist in what he termed a "sailor pose" while he beat his meat digging the sight of mine.

We made it a few times more in New York and then he brought me to New Haven late one night and on the train to Yale told me about the fag walks on campus and the bars and the freshmen who cruised him and about the queens on the swimming team. With all that, why did he need me?

"Let us go then, you and I, when the evening is spread out against the sky like a patient etherized upon a table; let us go, through certain half-deserted streets, the muttering retreats of restless nights in one-night cheap hotels and sawdust restaurants with oyster-shells . . ."

He asked me to lie naked on the couch across from him in his living room, while he sat, dressed, with reading glasses, and behind him a bookshelf full of many books, and he read Eliot's *Prufrock*. To tell you the truth, I could not get into it, the poem, it did not make any sense to me, sounded old mannish, if you know what I mean, but the sound of his voice, and the windows open to the sound of people in the neighborhood away, and, more, the odor of trees, like you never catch in New York City. Well, first it made me think of and get lonesome for the Rector in Chelsea and his family; however, as he read, I thought back on Evanston and the beach under the elm trees at night along the lake and Parker's voice coming to me from across the sand. I felt cheap lying on the couch naked like a statue or something, like a stripper on Ninth Avenue, while he poesied on, glanced over the book at me, and I could tell he was digging it, me lying there. I was a fantasy fulfilled, every humpy freshman in every Intro to Am Hist course he ever taught, brought home and revealed unwrapped—the basket the eyes staggered at under the cloth from the front of the room, youth legs in levis at their desks intent—and being *truly* educated, like Socrates must have done it, right? in Greece with the naked athletes who were not only jocks but smart kids no less who read poetry and played flutes.

"...*No! I am not Prince Hamlet, nor was meant to be*..."

I yawned. It was bore. I wanted to get the business over with and, too late for the train, hit the sack and sleep. To shut him up I started playing with myself, that is I took my cock in hand and moved the skin back and forth, getting it hard. He faltered in the reading, and struggled on. "...*I have seen them riding seaward on the waves combing the white hair of the waves blown back*..."

"I can only do it like once a night, once *good*. If it comes it goes." I grinned over at him.

"Wait a minute. Let me finish. '...*We have lingered in the chambers of the sea by sea-girls wreathed with seaweed red and brown till human voices wake us, and we drown.'* " I started to pant loud, tugging away like a fisher pulling in his nets.

"Just one more," he said, getting up and kneeling down in front of the bookshelves and pulling out a couple of volumes.

"Man, I've had it. I am *tired,* man, like I've been on my feet all day on the fucking street. And it's *hot* on that fucking street. . . ." I sat up.

"Listen," he said, and kneeling there he finally found one that drove into me, for I was open to sentiment that night, my mind drawn back like a curtain-skin, far back. *"Now hollow fires burn out to black . . ."* Housman, and this was how he read him, his voice deep, slowly, slowly, *". . . and lights are guttering low; square your shoulders and lift your pack and leave your friend and go. Fear not, lad, nought's to dread, look not left nor right: in all the endless road you tread there's nothing but the night."*

He looked at me. He knew he had me there. Grim poem, sentimental, which was probably why I liked it. It fit to me. That was what he wanted, to have me *listen,* to change me somehow in his vision from streetboy to sensitive man, as if they were exclusive of each other. That way I was coupled into his liberal Excuse: they-would-all-love-poetry-if-only-they-had-the-chance, and, there-but-for-fortune-go-you-and-I. You know the melody? He made me into a student. That he could relate to, and that he could feel he was corrupting.

We went upstairs where the bedrooms were. His wife was in Indiana visiting her old lady. He showed me her picture. Plump young lady, plump American young lady with teased up hair and heavy costume jewelry and wing-tipped glasses studded with rhinestones, and a timid smile.

"She chased me. *Years!* When she had me nailed, when we were married, suddenly sex did not interest her. She is Norwegian, a Lutheran. They are very stubborn people. She does not like sex very much. I guess that is why you are here." He was lying, about the sex part anyway, about that being the reason I was there. It had nothing to do with his wife.

"Is that why?" I asked, thinking the reason, *my* reason was cash on the line. He took the question to mean that I had been offended.

"No, no, even if we had a good sex life I would still want you here. I *like* you." Hand on the shoulder, professorial. He smiled. I felt like a pupil browning his teach.

We went into the master bedroom where he and his wife slept. A double bed. The sheets smelled of cologne. I lay on the bed, on my back, put my arms behind my head and spread my legs, and looked at the ceiling, and he said, "Wait a minute. I forgot something."

He left and returned with the baby boy in his arms. The kid was about a year old and asleep. He lay the baby down on the bed beside me and Cooper got erect, I never saw a man so hungry, and Cooper crawled in between my legs, and started licking away, making moaning sounds, taking my prick in his mouth and working it, clumsily, in his hurry scraping his teeth against the skin like a non-pro, and the baby woke up and started to cry and I reached over, while his old man did me, and pulled the baby next to me, the baby very soft, and that moment I really, desperately wanted to have my own baby, the want ached through me, and I hated Cooper and as he sucked I shoved my groin into his mouth trying to work my prick deep enough into his throat so it hurt, so it gagged him. He was unfazed. The baby in my arms, the baby grabbed my finger and sucked on it. Like father like son.

chapter nine

FANTASTIC, the Port Authority Bus Terminal in Manhattan, like an imperial monument to America, containing inside its shell what America had come to be—better than Grant's Tomb or the Statue of Liberty since it was a living thing and people were vulnerable inside of it, hated being there, like being in America. (You have to leave home to meet America. Home, anyone's home, is always somewhere else but in his country.) People wanted to pass through it fast to safety where there was no safety outside of it. For it was too familiar, familiar and out of joint, the Port Authority Bus Terminal, like every strange city. It was big and crowded. It came in on you, against you, as the late Penn Station never did. It had no secret corners. It was a very American place. Except that it never rained inside the Port Authority Bus Terminal.

I met Tutu there. Romantic, yes? About four in the morning in the bar at closing when the place was inhabited by pushers and beatout hustlers and old people and kids with no bread who had missed the last bus. She was wearing a mink sweater with nothing under it, and a pair of bright yellow pants, the color of lemon sherbet. Her hair was cut very short, like a boy's, and it was the color of her pants. She sat at the bar. I had on a pea jacket and a navy hat. I ordered a cup of coffee at a booth and the lights went up in the bar, hurting my eyes, and she said, "Sonofamotherfuckingbitch. Turn down the damn lights!"

I followed her lead. "Turn down the goddamn lights!" The lights stayed up, but Tutu noticed me, nearly fell off the stool when she saw me, she stared and squinted and sort of peeked her eyes around me, and then tears came to her eyes and she held firm, refusing to give way. (I remember once Parker and I got into a fist fight with some neighborhood street toughs. I was kicked in the stomach and I fell to the ground. The boys ran. Parker held me up and, as he did, he kept asking me if I was all right. I nodded that I was. I refused to admit to him that I was hurt, even though for twenty minutes I could not talk being out of breath and my stomach hurt making it painful to walk, and tears formed in my eyes. I would not admit to it. "You have no sympathy for your body," he commented. He was right.) She gazed at me as if she were hurt and was locking the hurt inside, not opening to it. Renouncing it.

After a while she stumbled over to my table, a little under with the booze, and stammered out, "I thought you were dead." Not a nice thing to say, even though she meant it well, said it in short, curt jolts like she was spitting out prune pits.

I looked at her. I shook my head. Another crazy. A

terminal case. It was too early in the morning to play games with screwball ladies in mink sweaters.

She stammered on. "When were you born?" She would not go away, like a panhandler on the street insisting on a quarter when you were in a rush to somewhere and he kept nagging after coins jingling in your pockets, coins you knew he heard. She stared, trying to catch my eye, to connect, giving me little knowing looks, as if I actually knew what the hell she wanted yet would not come across with it because I was a born tease.

"When were you born? *When?* What *day?* What *hour?* Christ! DON'T YOU EVEN KNOW WHEN THE HELL YOU WERE BORN?"

"Yeah, lady. I know." I told her when I was born. She nodded, her suspicions confirmed. She shoved a picture into my hand and glanced at me, down at the picture, over to me again.

"So?" It made no sense. The picture was a photo of her and a young man in shorts standing by the ocean. There was a beach umbrella in the background. Only the young man was smiling. The picture looked about twenty years old.

"It's *you!*" excited, announcing it like I had won a magazine contest. "Remember! Greece! 1948! Your *birthday!*"

"I never been to Greece, lady. I never even been to Jersey City, for that matter. It aint me."

"But it is, it is!" We tangled like that for a few minutes. The more I denied it the more she was convinced. I *looked* like him (a little around the eyes. My hair was lighter and I was better looking). I *talked* like him. We had the same birthday. Same height, same shoe size. We had a hell

97

of a lot in common, except I was at least twenty years younger than him.

Tutu bought me breakfast, something I never refused, and gave me a slip of paper with her name and address on it and told me to meet her at her pad the next night at eleven. I said I needed forty dollars for tuition (I usually gave that line to women since they could not bring themselves to call it by its name, stud fee) thinking forty dollars would put her off. It did not. When she left I thought about it. It seemed so goddamn improbable.

Tutu maintained an apartment, a loft actually, in an old tenement building in SoHo near the East Village. It was a dump from the outside. You had to climb five flights of stairs to reach it. Once inside it was another world.

When I arrived she met me at the door wearing the same clothes she was wearing in the picture—baggy slacks, a white, high-collared blouse, and sandals. She led me inside and sat me on the floor. "Nice," she remarked generally. Nice it wasn't. Weird it was.

The walls were covered with blue satin hangings, like curtains, billowing from fans in the windows behind them. The ceiling was painted sky blue with puffs of clouds. There were large vases scattered around full of grass and hash and decks of smack on the tables, and from all sides came whirling lights and screens on which slides played and dangling from the ceiling were hundreds of dolls at the end of strings which moved in the currents of air, throwing shadows on the ceiling, incense swirling around them. The floor was carpeted in some kind of soft, furlike stuff.

I sat on a pile of pillows and she asked me to get undressed. A reasonable request. I pulled off my clothes and sat down again, the fur feeling funny on my ass, sensuous. She handed me a bottle of wine and instructed me to drink. She moved around the loft dragging various things for me to see and play with: a small exquisitely crafted crystal doll's house; a feather duster made of birds' wings; a painted egg with a glass window in its wall and through it I could see two people-dolls making love; an album with the photos of nude youths looking starkly passive, straight ahead, each of them standing alone in a field before a mound of earth. "They're all dead," she said blankly. "Nazi victims. Jews. Poles. Look, all of them, all of them died horribly. Plucked from life like flowers. Plucked from life." Her tone was in sharp contrast to the game of bringing toy-things for me to play with, like children in a sandbox.

She took off her clothes very matter-of-factly, the way one does when one is alone before a bath. She pulled a small chair over close to me. She was in her late forties and she had stayed together well, her breasts were large and remarkably firm, only her thighs had slackened and aged. Her face was hard, tight, her cheekbones high. She spoke in a very high, childlike voice, bell-like, she trilled, her voice breaking often as if she were hoarse, as if it took great effort and strength to speak. I noticed, as we talked, that she kept moving her hands against each other, twisting her fingers together as if her hands were swollen and itched, chattering rapidly like a phonograph record spinning too fast, intensely, and then she drifted off into

99

silence. A speed freak. Ten years she said she was on it.

"Not bad," she said, noticing me studying her body, "Pretty much like I looked in Greece, don't you think?" She moved her hands over her body like a dance in a blue sequence at the Metropole, hands cupping her breasts from below offering them, then one hand sliding down toward her crotch, pressing her thighs. I watched. I was hot.

"You're not him. I know it," momentarily she was onto the deadman routine, touching the subject and drifting away from it, probing and moving back, letting it go, the truth out, with exhaled breath, like someone who has gripped a lie for many years finally trusting someone, or fatigued overmuch to maintain it any longer, and releasing it, falsehood, releasing it like you free a bird from your hand. It was a lovely admission, the way she said it, like a child confessing to a petty wickedness. We had been talking about the weather, or rather she had been. "It's hot. Unusually hot this late in the season. It is almost this hot in Southern Europe. You're not him. I know it. You are not him, but like him. What can I say. He lost his head." She giggled and then suppressed it. It was over my head, the meaning. "He liked little boys. Very young boys. Dark little boys. Do you like boys? No? An accident." She was musing now, drifting, and I could not fathom what was true in what she said. "The Land Rover turned over and cut him off ... like a young tree cut down ... the sun was so goddamn hot and so bright and the hills ... the road itself ... dust, everything was white like winter but frightfully hot ... white dust on the windshield ... I gathered

him up. Yesterday . . ." She stopped, like a monologue interrupted in a play, contrived. "I'll be back."

She went into another room behind some draperies, and
I watched her go, her ass moving rhythmically, grinding.
Returning, she carried a syringe and laughing jabbed the
needle into her stomach and laughing pressed in the high
and laughing withdrew it. Looking back on it, it seems
overly dramatic, except her laugh robbed it of drama, for
her laugh was shy, sheeting over terror. I felt very sorry
for her, sorry as I had felt for Doris dry and scratching on
the cool linoleum floor, dying. It aint worth forty bucks,
that is what I thought, not for this sight. Abstracting it:
poor and breaking country dream-tripping wrecked and
threading out life span by span for nothing that would
ever be alive. My old man.

She moved in front of me and leaned over, with her
hands on her knees, and kissed me, her breasts bobbing
against my shoulders. I reached up and put my arms
around her neck and drew her down against me and kissed
her deep and ran my hand over her back and against her
ass and under it between her legs to her moist sex and
caressed her. As we were held there, a lady, maybe seventy
years old, strolled in. "Hello, children," she said, and
moved across the room, kicking off her shoes, and carrying
a yapping terrier dog under her arm.

"One moment, children," she continued, and strode
regally over to me and extended her hand. "I am Countess
B———." I kissed her hand, a German sounding name,
foreign sounding anyway. It was like a play. The three of
us remained in position looking at one another for explana-

tion, as if one of us had missed his cue and we were waiting for the absent line. The silence lasted too long, the Countess finally breaking it, turning from us, "Continue, children. Just like old times, Tutu, just like old times." The Countess crossed to a sofa near us and I noticed, for the first time, that the furniture was made of parts of animals, at least the arm rests were formed of small animal heads, foxes, rabbits. Dried and hideous.

"Tutu, he's the one, isn't he? I would recognize him anywhere, especially in the raw." The Countess giggled. "Seymore," she said, talking to the terrier, "Do you think the children are charming together again after how long? When was his last appearance, Tutu, a year ago? He came as a waiter then. Oh, I do remember, I remember everything. Even the war." Tutu pulled closer to me and took my right hand in hers and moved it down under her and slid one of my fingers, as if it were an object, inside of her.

"I am bored, Seymore, frightfully bored." The Countess lay back on the sofa kicking pillows to the floor, hoisting up her dress, spread her legs, and pulled the dog by the ears in close to her. The Countess began to hum to herself as the dog played. It disgusted me, which was because I was frightened by it. I did not know how I was supposed to respond.

Tutu lay back on the floor before me and I lay on top of her and reached down between us and centered my prick and moved inside of her in a rush and pushed hard and fast and she made no sound whatsoever, simply closed her eyes and rolled her muscles with mine while I tried to come strong and quickly and to move my lips, awkwardly, over her face, touching her eyelids with my mouth, while the Countess hummed to herself and broke off from time to time to make a comment, ". . . he is what, Tutu, the fifth or the sixth? It is so difficult, sweetheart, to keep up with Douglas' reincarnations. It is *tiresome*, Tutu, although *God knows* I try, how *hard* I try. For *your* sake, sweetheart. I try. They do come and go . . . Douglas has improved with years, unlike us. . . ."

I drank wine from the bottle. Tutu put on hard rock music and danced around me on the rug; she looked stoned, acted it, and I followed her movement as she found a scarf and like an oriental dancer she waved the scarf and drew it across her body as she danced, draped it over me and pulled it away, her body one motion, undulating, and I got an erection and it hurt a little bit because I had just come minutes before and the head of my tool was tender. Close to me she came, and I moved each time forward to try and lick her sex which glistened, "Tell me you love me. Tell me that and you can go."

"Don't be a fool, sweetheart. He *never* loved you." And again: "Don't be naughty, Tutu, he *loves* only *boys*."

"Tell me. Once."

I looked up at her. It was not sexy anymore. I was so tired and I wanted to leave, tired and fazed not because of the wine and sex, tired of the scene and the madness and the artifice. I felt sorry for her. I did not believe I could afford it. Simple as that.

"I love you, baby," I lied. It was not hard to do.

She stopped dancing. Wide eyes. I did not want her to cry, God, not that, that I could not take. It was enough. Forty bucks. I had earned it. "Say it again." Words, what do they mean? She squatted before me and lay her arms around my neck, her right leg bumping against my half-erection, her breasts touching my chest. She closed nearer, and put her forehead against mine. In a whisper. "Tell me, once more."

The Countess: "He never gave a damn about you. You were *shit* to him, the pansy bastard."

I laughed. It was funny, the Countess. Laughing I said, "I love you, baby," more to spite the Countess than to convince Tutu.

Tutu danced away. I got up and pulled on my clothes, kept looking down to avoid seeing her. Unfunny now. I took out the money she had put in my pocket, the first time I ever did, and left it on the cushions.

Tutu caught me at the door. "Don't leave. We're only playing."

I hesitated. "I'll be back."

"Where are you going?" expecting a lie, I could see it in her face.

"I'm hungry. Going to get some food."

"Bring me back something, some breakfast."

"Sure." Another promise.

I saw Tutu one more time, at a reception at an art gallery I was taken to about a year later.

She was sitting with an older, very distinguished looking man on a bench to the side. "Hi," I said. She was spaced, unable to remember.

"I don't know who you are," confused, wary. "What do you want?" a trace of the bitch-edge on her voice. She glanced over to the man seated next to her, looking for support.

"Nothing, lady." I turned, and I thought I should go back and get my forty dollars, but I did not.

chapter ten

LATE fall. At a party on Central Park West, given by a left-liberal for people who supported the civil rights movement. A lot of writers there, and editors, looking as they always do at parties given in the evening of a work day, looking beat out and sliding half out of the room toward the commuter train with three martinis too many, always.

Andrew, a black from South Carolina (his ambition: to integrate the men's room at the Trailways Bus Depot in Richmond, Virginia). I ran into Andrew on 42nd Street, playing FASCINATION. There because it was warm in the shop and it was open late at night and he was in a sense addicted to tossing the pink rubber ball and staring at it bouncing toward the winning hole. Andrew was growing more political, angrier, planning Freedom Rides sometime, a return to South Carolina sometime, and planning, as I said, like my old man used to *plan,* to get a CORE group together and integrate that bus depot. Every time he traveled through Richmond he was denied use of the cleaner, bigger *whites only* men's room. That animated him, the obsession to take a piss in that place; of millions of American bathrooms that particular one he had to pick a quarrel with. A lover's quarrel, as Frost would say. He loved talking about the john in Richmond, imagining what it was like inside, like Jack rapping about his Duke of Earl and the castle in Wales.

"I don't even know what goddamn color it's painted," he moaned, "I don't even know what its walls are like, probably green, don't you think, or maybe blue, lot of Dixie piss joints is blue, robin egg blue. Must be at *least* ten piss slots in the damn tearoom, maybe more, arranged *geometrically* along the wall. Stalls on the other side, with marble slabs for partitions most likely, and black, or maybe fake stone, or maybe wooden seats, like in an outhouse, rednecks is partial to wooden seats. . . . Been inside the Statute of Liberty," he wailed, "been in the nation's Capitol, but never inside that friggin' john."

Andrew and I hit the party together, he leaving me to score among the guests. He was there to talk politics. You guessed it. It was Parker I was near in his color.

I talked for a time with Coretta, who had also been invited unofficially by Andrew, but Coretta had to split early to get to her restaurant job, late already, and the host making her feel distinctly out of place, even though writers and other arty types like a few queers and freaks around to amuse them.

Some fag editor sized me up and gave out with his phone number. I didn't say anything, but when he asked, "Do you write, young man?" I laughed because it was such a clumsy buy.

A lady professor, who lived in Princeton and was there

with her husband, came over and talked with me, or at me, dropped names of writers she knew which I did not recognize and was therefore singularly unimpressed. She took my phone number.

Her husband came up after his wife had moved on, I noticed him standing in the distance watching. He gave me the same line as his wife had given me, but he did not do it as well. It sounded fake and nervous. He dropped the same tired names, but my mind was wandering because I was thinking of Coretta and how I ought to leave before midnight and take the train down to the Village and see her since she looked as if she were on one mean trip, and thinking that this party was a dud, no paying customers unless it was the lady professor from Princeton and her husband (their name was Slugmore), who looked about ten years younger than she, looked unhousebroken with the culture shit he was laying out in the room, looked about my age. I sized him up as a closet queen.

Two hours later. In the kitchen. A small room with a counter (against which I leaned) on one side with cabinets hung on the wall above it. A stove, sink, refrigerator on the other side, directly across from where I stood. I had a drink on the counter beside me. The kitchen was cool and quiet.

I was there alone about ten minutes when two men came into the kitchen. One was a short, heavyset man, looking like a football player gone to pot. The other man was tall, well built, younger than his friend. A Puerto Rican, maybe a boxer, or a bouncer or a bodyguard. The small man said, as they walked in, "Jesus Christ! Here's the fucking booze!" He glanced at me as he made a hard, sweeping movement toward the bottle of scotch on the top of the refrigerator.

He and his friend stood across from me, I playing it silent like a hustler—silence the score needs, silence to play inside and build again what he remembers and seeks to possess and never quite owns—the small man doing most of the talking, bitching about the party, the fools at the party, and then talking about writing, and then about boxing, all the while pouring on the sweet charm. As he talked he kept inspecting me, talked to his friend but glanced at me from the corner of his eye, sizing me up. The small man was wearing a very thick, tweed, three-piece suit, a buttondown shirt, the collar buttons undone, his tie pushed over to the side of his neck, his hair short and dark and curly, wiry, beginning to gray. Light, intense eyes. As he talked to his boxer-bouncer-bodyguard companion, he maintained a kind of bobbing, boxerlike motion, rocking on the balls of his feet, sometimes one hand, sometimes both thrust Jack Kennedy style in his jacket pockets, the coat itself pulled out of shape, hanging stretched at the bottom in front. He talked fast, his mouth tight as he talked, his lips very consciously molded over and covering his teeth, something like Humphrey Bogart talking. As he spoke and drank he slipped into a very bad, very clipped Southern accent, his speech getting dirtier, his diction less precise, a trace of the maudlin, the bathetic, entering like fog into his now-Southern dialect, and with it the fog edged by the hint of suppressed anger. Pugnaciousness.

"What ya lookin' at? Ya lookin' at me, Sam Parsons? Ya lookin' at Sam Parsons?" the small man said, wheeling toward me, as he turned vaguely throwing his drink toward the top of the refrigerator, missing it by a foot. It smashed at his feet on the floor. The boxer-bouncer-bodyguard laughed. "Fuck da motherfuckin' drink, fuck da motherfucker!" Parsons swung his hands awkwardly at his side, and it occurred to me that the man, maybe forty years old, maybe older, was painfully self-conscious about his body and was trying to throw it at me, in my face, because he really did not like his body, was constrained by it, betrayed by its thudding lack of grace, did not find his body at all attractive, or himself attractive, and was trying to pin it on me.

"What ya lookin' at?" he demanded again, stepping closer.

I did not say anything. I stood, leaning against the counter, my drink beside me, my hands loose at my side. I figured the guy's drunk and the guy's lonely and the guy wants a fight, which I aint about to give him, for if the guy wants me he is going to pay me for me, he aint going to get me cheap by wrestling like high school kids in the goddamn kitchen.

Parsons moved closer, unsteady. He stared at me defiantly, falsely, a put-on where I knew and he knew it was a game that he had to make because he was drunk and full of dislike for himself and blind before the knowledge of his own physical cowardice. He bobbed his head down, looking up at me, his eyebrows pulled down in a comic attempt at a tough expression, his eyes peering up under his eyebrows. He stood, head lowered, and lifted his hands and parried like a boxer in the air, and then, with a quick, very sweet, plaintive, almost timid smile, he threw a light punch against my right shoulder. It didn't hurt. He moved back.

Again he shadow boxed the air, glancing over his shoulder at his companion, saying, "The motherfucker thinks he's a big man," and then looking back at me, giving me his forty-year-old boyish smile, notifying me with it that the statement was a press release directed toward our audience and did not really count as truth as far as we were concerned. The Dead End Kid grinning, the scrapping punk ageing and not liking it and grinning, the good-natured pub grinning. Again he did an inelegant boxer's dance, bobbed, bounced toward me on the balls of his feet, and planted another punch against my shoulder. This one was hard.

Parsons moved away, playing me like a bull. I thought, now what the hell is this son of a bitch after, what does he want, does he want me to lay him out, he lonely and playing for attention, he playing roughhouse stud for his companion. I figured he was a writer or an editor or something connected with that business for what he had rapped about earlier. I knew he was a drunk, that I could see. Man, if there was one thing I had sympathy for it was a drunk.

This time he made his boxer's dance toward me. No smile this time. He was pushing for the limit, knowing no bell would save him. He moved in close, bobbing, throwing little punches in the air, like a boxer jabbing in the ring, in close and I drew back my arm, and he saw me draw back my arm, but he moved in closer and I saw he was breathy hard spent, and I could smell the liquor on his breath and it was funny, because he seemed like someone about my age who had gone fat and bad and weak early and was now full of troubles yet trying to stay *in* the club, thinking everybody he respected and hated was laughing behind his back regardless of how they protested their respect for him, he had to stab at winning by their rules, humanly, with the fists, the only rules he knew and respected, and to win by losing, win because he was willing to fight knowing he was not able to win. And it was the impossibility of the odds which proved his courage.

He moved toward me, closer, and I threw my fist into his belly. He groaned and fell toward me, his knees buckling, his companion laughing, and as he fell he grabbed my knees to right himself, to escape the humiliation of landing flat on the floor like a rummy, not a fighter, like some beer-bellied over-the-hill boxer hearing bells in his ears. I reached down and lifted him below the shoulders, my hands supporting him under the armpits, his body warm and booze sweated, the wool cloth damp. As I lifted him up, he helped raise himself—one heavy mother—by gripping my legs for support, his hands climbing me drunkenly, above the knees, on the thighs, his warm, thick butcher hands. Finally up and grinning at me, his arms thrown around me, smiling and beaming like a kid.

"Only fuckin' man in the fuckin' house!" he shouted, looking over at his friend. I was about a foot taller than Parsons, but he kept his arm locked around my body and edged me out of the kitchen and into the living room, convinced, I think, that I was as drunk as he and he was physically supporting me as we went.

"THE ONLY FUCKIN' MAN IN THE FUCKIN'

PLACE!" he shouted at the crowd in the room, bouncing on his toes as he did, his right hand jabbed into his jacket pocket, his left slapping me vigorously on the back, his head held high and back, grinning up at me like I was some kind of rare trophy, some nearly extinct species he had brought back, *alive*, singlehandedly! from a safari. "MY PAL! THE ONLY FUCKIN' MAN IN THE PLACE! WHO'S GOT BALLS ENOUGH TO TACKLE HIM ... (dramatic silence) ... OR ME!" I stood beside him, my feelings a combination of embarrassment and pride. Mr. Slugmore sat stewed at the far end of the room, away from his wife, staring at me blurred, a faintly condescending grin creeping on his face. Both fools, I guess he was thinking, and my vanity made me suppose that he thought I was a lost fool to his bed that night.

Parsons grabbed another drink and began to march around me, hoisting his drink like a torch in the air, and sang, off key, *"Mine eyes have seen the glory of the coming of the Lord, he is trampling ..."* He danced about me, making little sideswiping punches. I got carried away by his good humor and began singing with him and laughing, the two of us half-trotted and half-danced in a small circle, grinning at each other like survivors after a battle.

"Sam!" His wife. Ten years younger and half a foot taller. "Let's go, Sam." Parsons continued to dance, avoiding her. She tried to catch him, but after watching him nimbly side-step her each time, she walked away from him. She turned on me, she in a snit over the scene. "See what you've done?" she shouted, glaring at me, "You got him drunk, and now you've got him dancing around like a Russian bear!"

"Lady," I said, laughing, thinking he really did look like a Russian dancing bear, "I never did see your Sam before."

"Bullshit!" she said, and pushed past me. She sauntered off, and I watched her go, and I thought, seeing the handsome way she tossed her lovely ass, old Samboy, you got yourself some fine piece of woman. Got to say that for you, Sam, drunk or not, you sure won a fine woman.

She returned, carrying his overcoat. She caught Sam, turned him around and dumped his coat over him. He sobered up, suddenly. "Come, Sammy. Beddiboo time." Like a mother hauling in her kid.

Sam Parsons left, reluctantly trailing his wife. At the door, seconds before he exited, he whipped around, sneaking a quick prank before his wife caged him for the night. "Boy!" he shouted at me, "You're the *only* mother in the entire room with *balls!*" I got to tell you, I felt like I came into my kingdom that night, what with Mrs. Slugmore and the others grinning at me kind of envious because somehow in their knick-knack cultural world I had made it by a fluke to center stage for a moment. I sure felt good.

chapter eleven

ANDREW's old lady in South Carolina was sick with tuberculosis, or "consumption," as Andrew termed it, giving the illness a Thomas-Mann-Magic-Mountain class non-jive connotation, and his mind was turning around having to travel back to the old folks at home, and not wanting to because, living on the street and being in the Movement (which for him was not burning down the prison but swiping the keys to the kingdom from the Man) as he was, in his time and in his place feeling veridical pride in his blackness ("negritude," to paint the concept with a French Colonial nuance), he had found his nation in his people in their city north in Harlem.

As days passed in our friendship, black nationalism spread like night into Harlem, with less alacrity into the other ghettos reaching Bed-Sty with somewhat less force and immediacy, but with identical historic necessity and sufficiency. Harlem was like the shaft of a wide and impossibly long penis that hardened with pride first at the bottom and then continued building hard as a fist, never quite reaching potency in its penis head, and in its rise scaring the hell out of whitey, although only three-quarters rigid and unused.

Andrew found in his people and their pride his identity apart from us, me. Inside of him was some small country, former colony-client state, flushed with pride, his soul, which grew and spread and annexed and conquered and divided him from me, from us, as they had once divided Parker from himself, giving him strength.

It was not that Andrew changed, but that he expanded. Like one of the Japanese paper flowers you drop into a fish bowl and watch it absorb the liquid and fill the globe. Hustling, while he hit the streets, was a *means* to something very real and very serious to him. Getting the coins to organize and make his Freedom Ride to Richmond, after Bull Run, after the Union rout, to ride into it in his own Shermanesque sweep making sure, in that antiquated place, that the South would not rise again. No more. This was like two years or more after Freedom Rides went out of style with the riots, assassinations and the tromping pigs. So in a sense I envied my spade man with his country found and building and his mind made up about our America: free, in freedom from the myth, from the ambiguity. And all the while, him, on the other side of where I, we, stood telling me to come on in the river and make the crossing from the stormy banks because Jordan's water was warm and smelled sweet and it would clean your perfect body ... him humming, I remember our sitting in the late afternoon in a bar on 125th Street in the early winter with the thin sunlight coming in through the windows, through the dark yellow plastic sunshade on the windows, and the dark yellow sunlight fall-

ing on his naked arms, making his brown skin appear hot
and otherworldly—and making me, with a honky imagination, think of slavers, Congo drums, human sacrifice, per-
spiring, coercive sex in the African bush in the humid, wet,
wind-whipped elephant grass at night, with an obese
Sidney Greenstreet, dressed in a planter's white suit,
lounging in a wicker chair on a nearby veranda under
swaying palm trees, a black woman slave fans him in the
insufferable equatorial heat and he silently schemes his
evil plots, grunting, frowning, waiting for Bogey to paddle
upriver smuggling rifles and elephant tusks, the dead,
tropical night air severed by pagan wails—and Andrew
humming, and me mouthing the words as he hummed,
and me thinking about sister Lily mouthing Parker's
words, *If I forget thee . . .* him humming *Suzanne.*

We were sitting in a bar on 125th Street waiting for
Vanessa, Andrew's white chick, and Pauline, mine, to meet
us. Saturday afternoon. Dusk. It had stopped snowing
about an hour before. Through the dark yellow sunshade
of the bar window the snow in the street looked yellow.
Andrew said it reminded him of the color of a harvested
field, orange-yellow in the setting sun.
  "Meeting with some righteous cake-eaters tonight,"
Andrew said, referring to the rich liberals he was trying to
hit for coins to bankroll his personal Freedom Ride. This
was going to be his own show. He was not working with
any civil rights organization. There was no civil rights
organization—except the NAACP, which was Uncle Tom
—which was interested in Freedom Rides anymore, especially a Freedom Ride whose sole purpose was the integra-

tion of one lousy bathroom in the Trailways Bus Depot in Richmond, Virginia. That was not exactly an event of earthshaking importance. "All I got to do is get me a bus, get the brothers and sisters together, and I's *off*." He grinned at me, pressing my wrist with his hand. He was nervous. He had talked about it for a long time.

"Are you sure you want to go? Man, you know what you're going to face in that hick town? Pigs, rednecks, *real* Americans? You know?"

"Do *I* know?" he asked, laughing, and, with his laugh, putting me down. My question, coming out of my white face, was, in terms of his Southern history, patronizing. "I *from* there, south of the Mason-Dixon, old Dixie cupsville. That is home turf, Baby. Don't I know, mister, don't I *know* the way they murder and make no sound. No notice. You just ups and disappears, liquidated like in Russia. Well, maybe I'm smarter than those white mothers. At least I know they gonna try nothing mean in Richmond, not with the pack of white liberals I'm bringing along. After that, back home, that's when they show the old hand." He was quiet a moment. After a time he looked up at me, placing his hand gently on my cheek, caressing it, "You won't be along then, old buddy, and you won't hear of me no more. You'll be peddling your white ass as always, or you'll turn straight. We *different* races, buddy, with different things owed to different people. Your time's gonna come, too."

"You shouldn't go," I said, worried for him, not knowing what was in his plans, knowing that his pain was direct and real and too much to play Harlem games away from Carolina.

"Don't give me no liberal crap. That's *you*, baby. *Inside* you are a liberal mother just like every other honky in this town. Liberal because you never think about nothing with your brains except the next pigeon, except setting him up. And when you do something for the cause you do it believing you do it for your friends. Well, mister, you gotta learn better where your friends is. Not all the black cats, not all the whites, not everyone, just because they's poor or talk the language, not everyone's your friend. You got to learn to tell the victim *inside*, to smell him out and stay on *his* side of the bad street. That you gotta do. You *white!* And you come from white people out there somewhere with the cows. You gotta get yourself together, baby, and make up inside that head what it mean to be white in whitey's country, what it mean to be white and out of it, selling your meat like a nigger in your own country. You make that out, and you make out what that mean to your black brothers, how you act to your brothers, where and when for *them* you can act like a friend and not a honky, you make that out in your crazy head."

"What you crapping on me for, what've I done?" I was angered by his preaching.

"Listen, baby," he said, his voice tender, "You only a street hustler *part* time. You in for parlor games now. You moving among some rich cats, fat trips in the country to parties, on the avenue, all that shit. You better off than you let on." He laughed. It was true. I was beginning to score sometimes with cake-eaters, doing the party circuit, my named passed around and most of my trade coming through contacts arranged by phone. "You slipping over the line between a whore and a hustler, you starting to think like a Kennedy," he said, knowing how I loved the Kennedys, how I used Jack Kennedy's martyrdom as a symbol of what a good white was like, what we at our best, were capable of. "You be careful or you'll wake to discover you's one cheap slut, one most unfree, pimpless, male hooker."

"Christ!" really pissed angry, "What the hell this have to do with what we were rapping about? We were rapping about the fact that you shouldn't go back South, that's what we was rapping about."

"You *know* that answer, sweetheart. Gotta go back home. First to Richmond and then home. I is *done* with these fucking streets and these fucking creep johns." Smiling again, proudly, "Aint scored in a month, baby. I is *un*-hooked." That surprised me, that he had not scored. "And I aint never again. They want black meat, shit, let them service the dinge baths or go without. This colored child aint putting out nothing at no price for them mothers. No, sir!"

Leaving us, in the winter, the worst drag season of the year when it was hard as hell to score any place with anything and some hustlers took to pushing grass and speed and stealing to eat, dreaming in the winter of the fun summer things to come, holding tight, trying to spread the coins and the will far enough to make it through to spring without selling out for good, going straight. For that, going straight, was death, the end of liberty, that was the end of self.

"What you living on, Andrew, if you aint making the street?"

"I got me a girl, that you know. And I got me a bank

account. And I got me a vision. That's what I got. What you got, old buddy, what you got but selling your rod to payoff queens, huh? What *future* you got, what vision? You is *used*, mister. You is one all around loser, that what you is, and when your beads read age, you gonna cross that street, you gonna leave the sweet meat rack without even a meal ticket unless you sell it, pack it in and sell the whole man, get ass-fucked like a bender by a butching lover. You can't stay commercial your life long, baby, not with the youngsters pressing in."

"What you *want* of me? You want me to go home with you? I aint no black, Andrew, I can't play your life."

"But you do already. How many of them Uncle Tom demonstrations you been on with me, how many? Five, six, at least that, with you not knowing the good from the bad and thinking the good was poor dead Kennedy and the bad was only hurting against your friends, the friends you could *see*. Remember knocking the shit out of them mothers in Times Square, you remember that?" I remembered, six American Nazi Party members in the early evening standing on the traffic island by the recruiting station in the Square and Andrew and me and two other street workers rolling over them, hitting them hard, one of the cocksuckers running and yelling for the cops, "Well, you are in the life now, in the city fighting the siege. . . ."

Vanessa and Pauline came in, interrupting Andrew. We greeted them. I tongue kissed Pauline deep, enjoying the public display. *"Don't,* honey, everybody *star*ing." We went to a booth in the back, sat down and ordered drinks, Pauline having a scotch and milk. "That's what Jackie Kennedy drinks," she informed us, "An article in *McCall's* says she drinks nothing but milk with scotch in it." I told her she was full of shit. "So is Jackie Kennedy then," she replied. Andrew laughed. Vanessa smiled. Three whites and a black in a spade bar. Beautiful sight.

We drank for about an hour, Andrew talking about the people who were putting up the five hundred bills needed to make the Freedom Ride, one of them a writer who hung around the college kids. The bar was crowded, almost entirely filled with blacks, a few black hookers sitting on the high stools by the front windows, sipping their drinks, passing the time until the night was right, peering into the windows, catching their reflection faintly in the glass, touching their massive, wildly dyed wigs with the tips of their fingers. Waiting. At the bar were two white cops, off duty, inside waiting too, for them it was payoffs from the pushers to keep clean for the coming week. The rest of the people in the room were black workers, a few hustlers, most of whom waved or nodded at us as they entered. I felt safe there with Andrew, much safer than I usually felt in Harlem, *any*where in Harlem. I was known by a few blacks, but I was far from safe. After leaving anytime with Andrew, I headed straight for the subway at night. In the day it was all right, but at night I was ill-at-ease for I did not know their city well enough to know where my limits lay. So I split.

One of the blacks at the bar came over and spoke quietly to Andrew. The man was wearing his hair natural and long, had African beads and sunglasses and a long robe over his suit. Andrew did not introduce me, and that I understood since, if he was really clean now, he would not want his black political friends to meet me. No one likes to be known as a whore once they go into another life. He and his friend went over to the bar. A few minutes later Andrew returned. He said his friend could not make the meeting tonight. It discouraged him for it signified a general lack of enthusiasm for his project on the part of the brothers. He was feeling low.

Vanessa sat beside him, her hand in his, and gradually she let her head, with its long auburn hair, rest on his shoulder. Twice he pushed her away. "Don't, Van," he said, brusquely. That I did not understand, since Vanessa was no sick guilty white mama needing a black man to feed her masochism. *He* had pursued her, as much as he pursued anyone.

"You want to go?" she asked him quietly. Pauline, next to me and feeling out of it because I had not moved to touch her, believing me to be embarrassed by her because she was white—and in sexual situations somehow many whites were defensive, wanting violation by a black—playing a hopeless game of pocket pool with my balls under the table, started to giggle nervously. "I don't know about Andrew, but *I* sure want to go. Let's have some *ac*tion!"

Vanessa was laying her head again on his shoulder and he, again, shoved it off. Irritated. Things on his mind. He stood up and went over to the bar.

"Where's he going?" Pauline said, in her own inscrutable way insulted by his leaving. I shrugged and got up and followed him.

Andrew stood talking to the black in the African robe who had stopped by the table. I went over and leaned against the back of the bar, but at sufficient distance to give Andrew privacy. While I stood there, a fat man walked by, dressed in a suit, a white man carrying a camel's hair overcoat on his arm. He walked rather hurriedly over to Andrew, interrupted the conversation. He put his hand on Andrew's shoulder. Andrew stepped back suddenly and said something to the fat man, who looked startled, and then, composing himself, raised his arm in the air and directed a faggy, sweeping limp wrist toward Andrew. "Oh, my *dear!*" was what I heard him say. The fat man left Andrew in a bit of a huff, passed by me and, glancing at me, gave me a faggot's cruising you're-one-of-us-mary look, feeling better perhaps because I was white and young, indicated Andrew with a flick of his head, leaned toward me, smelling of cologne. He said, "The silly nigger faggot. *Mercy be! Don't* those *darkies* put on airs!"

Later I asked Andrew who the fat man was. "Some old john. Been around a long time. Likes spade meat." He paused, shook his head angrily, "A real racist, that one." I felt enormous love for Andrew then, for what he was up against all his life. I felt kin to him, both of us hustlers, in a real sense outlaws in our country, and in our feud with the fat men, all those bastardly American users, the line was drawn strong, the rules displayed exactly. We were one with each other, Andrew and me. Solid.

That night, after the girls left, I walked to the subway alone. I saw the fat white man who had called Andrew a nigger faggot. Fix the pig's clock. I ambled by him. Glanced at him. Caught his eye. Walked a few paces more. Looked around, checking him out. Caught his eye once more. Cruised him. He was standing near the corner.

I stopped in front of a discount store. EASY CREDIT NO MONEY DOWN. Knowing I was being observed, I thrust my hands in my pockets, stood butch, studied the store window. The fat man turned, strolled by me, stopped a few feet away. Lit a cigarette. Peeked over at me. Edged toward me. I edged away. He moved again. Closer. Next to each other. I looked into the sales window. He stared at his shoes. I watched him reflected in the window. "You busy?" he asked, his voice low, tense, hesitant. After he spoke he coughed nervously.

"Why?" played it dumb, threading him out.

"I'm free tonight," he said. Big deal. Clumsy, that's what he was, and unwary. "We could do something. I have nothing to do tonight."

I took the chance. I was determined to set the bastard up. Not because I knew he had done damage to Andrew beyond the racist slur, but because he was white and Parker was black and I had bills to settle. I recognized that the payment had to be violent. I nailed him as a score, clumsy enough to be hungry in the winter with Manhattan full of available studs. There was in his person what I hated, more than the simple disgust a hustler feels toward his client, a detestation born in a rape of pride and in the truth, unacknowledged, that in the mortification was the kick, but hatred over his well-fed, moneyed body, his desperation and his lust which bloated itself licking manhood like sweat off our balls, fed eagerly on our youth, the angularity of our bodies, the dissembled and wholly false inappetence of our silence, on—and here lay the victimhood and the criminality, and here, it's true, we collaborated, like authentic whores, with the enemy—what remained untouched, ruthless and thus pure in the timbre of our manhood: the sticky promise of our violence. That is what I hated, the understanding that the fat men made me betray myself in giving way to rage.

Every score, ultimately, wanted to die. And I, with that fat man, broke the rules, as much as Willie broke the rules, by setting him up. I took the chance. I smiled.

"Like ten o'clock, man. Huh? In the . . . you know where the Seamen's Institute is? Huh? By the Battery? About ten o'clock there, in the lobby. I'll get a room." I had used it before.

He beamed. Incredulous. *"All night?"* Fat man felt he was loved.

I grinned, and rubbed my crotch with the palms of my hands as if I were whipping off come and, as I did, arched my groin suddenly. It blew his mind.

I walked away.

Nine-thirty. I dragged Pauline along as cover, over-coming her protests with the promise of a ride on the ferry, which she loved, telling her, "First I got to see a guy."

"What guy?"

"Just a guy."

"Well, what *kind* of guy?" She suspected I was planning on scoring quick before tending to her. She was right.

"A business partner," I said, remembering my old man.

We took the subway down to South Ferry, Pauline cozying up against me on the bench, proud of being out in public with her loverman. I dug Pauline. She was a good woman, a little on the plump side, married to some man I had never met, living out in Queens by the cemetery, working at Macy's in the lamp department. For months she had been trying to persuade me to swing out to Queens to see her three kids, every night telling me to ride out and I always putting it off. "He sleeps like a log, we can do it on the porch, no one will know," she said, in answer to my refusals.

The subway was overheated. Pauline was overheated, wearing a heavy blue coat, a wool scarf, mittens, a sweater and skirt, *two* pairs of nylon stockings (she claimed she needed two pair, her feet always swollen from standing all day among the lamps at Macy's).

Pauline and I arrived at the Seamen's Institute about an hour late. The institution—a YMCA type hotel and social center established by the Episcopal Church for sailors— was nearly empty. Not much business in winter. The fat pigeon was standing, smoking, by the elevators at the end of the lobby. I told Pauline to sit down and wait. She sat.

I walked over to the fat man, smiled at him, and went past him into the elevator. He followed. We left the elevator on the top floor, where the marine museum was, he tagging about a yard behind me. I walked to the exit and went out the door. Inside the stairwell I stopped. The fat man followed me and then he stopped. It was dark, the only light coming from a red exit sign above the door. The fat man was wearing a beige camel's hair overcoat, oxford shoes, a light gray suit. His face was like that of a little boy who had gone gray fifty years too soon. There were no wrinkles on his face. He smiled at me. He was nervous. He stood with his hands hanging limp at his side, his belly forward, his overcoat and suit appearing pink in the light. I thought of Peter Lorre making some midnight rendezvous with Humphrey Bogart to haggle over the Maltese Falcon; I thought of fat Southern planters meeting their young, black stud slaves in tobacco sheds at night to force them to sodomy.

"You got thirty bucks?"

"For what?" he asked, offended, a little frightened.

"For the room," sharply.

He dug inside his pocket and pulled out a roll of bills. He peeled three off and handed them to me. A chicken, Jesus Christ, a chicken at his age, paying before the merchandise was delivered. He wanted it bad. A sucker. My old man.

I grabbed the money and climbed the stairs. "Where we going?" he asked, and followed. To the top. Out onto the roof.

On the roof was a narrow landing which circled a lighthouse capped by an illuminated cross. It was cold outside, the wind was blowing strong off the harbor. I saw the lights of Staten Island in the distance, the Statue of Liberty rising by the Jersey shore, and beyond, darkness: the ocean.

"Andrew?" I asked, "You know Andrew?" I leaned casually against the wall of the lighthouse, unzipping my jacket. He stood directly across from me, his back to the guard railing, below him the street and, farther, the water.

"Who?"

"Andrew, the colored fellow you talked to at the bar," I said, my voice rough. It was cold and I was getting anxious, not simply because the situation was sexual but because its sexuality vibrated with potential violence.

"Oh," he said. He looked up at me and smiled, the wind ruffling his thinning hair, blowing wisps of it across his eyes, emphasizing in the darkness, modified only by the dim lighthouse beacon, the youthful quality of his face. I gazed at him, my hand inside my pants, my knit shirt raised above my navel, teasing him with my skin and hair, with my hand moving up and down. I thought, my feelings ambivalent, he has probably been fat all his life, all his goddamn life hating himself because he was fat and feeling out of it, lonely, because he had been a fat youth and now was a fat man grinding into late middle age. Funny, but man, I tell you for a moment I felt sorry for the slob.

"Oh, *that's* his name," he chuckled, moving close to me, reaching out very slowly with his hand toward my groin, "Funny name for a nigger." It was no funny name for no nigger.

I hit him in the face. He swung his body back, grabbing the railing with his arm. I kicked him in the crotch. Kicked him again. He groaned. Lay there in a pile groaning. "Motherfucker! Racist bastard!" He lifted his head, dazed, looking up at me.

"You want it?" I said, tough, so motherfucking tough. He looked at me, lifting his head, dazed, his mouth bleeding, his hands pressed into his crotch, he trying to comprehend where he was and who I was and what the hell had happened to make him hurt so bad. He groaned, his voice unusually high, high as a small boy's voice. Made me think of boys on playing fields yelling in their games.

A foghorn sounded on the harbor. Parker. It's so goddamn sick, I thought, meaning myself. Then he moaned very loud. I broke, feeling his hurt. "Wait," I said kneeling down, "wait, I'll give you some help," me going soft, weak on me, opening myself up. I placed my hands under his arms to assist him in rising, started to lift him, he being very heavy, the cloth under his armpits moist. He was conscious. He rubbed his right hand under his nose to catch the bleeding. He was conscious. "Awww," he moaned, sitting up, pushing my arms away. Then, glancing at my crotch, *reaching* for it. S&M mother. I sprang up. I kicked him in the mouth. "Motherfucker!" I yelled, and stamped his hands and groin. I was trembling and suddenly very cold.

"Look at *that!*" Pauline said, in the lobby, giggling, pointing at my crotch where my erection bulged under the cloth. Then I noticed it and noticed too his blood on my trouser leg.

Pauline and I took the ferry to Staten Island and back again, standing together in the wind on the front of the boat, my arms around her, her head resting sleepily on my shoulder with her hair flapping like a flag against my cheek in the air which smelled of the sea. Manhattan loomed and faded and I wondered why increasingly it seemed that in my wake was life left speckled with grudging violence, like spume on ocean water, and bad, one-hit empty sex and loneliness dawning in the need of others to tap me like woodsmen stripping maples. Nothing filled me unless the nascent emptiness, like an object in itself, making itself felt hard beside her on the boat, cloud-

ing off like gas into self-contempt and misplaced pity . . .
on the ferry feeling low, aching for my old man, no, for
something else sentimental and too good to be remembered truthfully which I missed but could not name. It was
Andrew, and Parker also, I was striking for, blackmen who
made me want to lash out to make me equal to their
courage. It was myself I was defending. For I, too, at
times wanted to die.

In my room. Emotionally exhausted, unable to get my
head together—it was by chance I knocked into the fat
man, he functioned like a class, depersonalized—like I had
taken three times too much librium and was drugged,
broken somewhere inside to the left, and blinding out the
thought of it with booze. I drank. And drank. Pauline lay
on my bed under the reading lamp, wearing only her
black bra, still on, her breasts pulled over it, the bra like
a black armor girdle across her chest, and her garter belt,
black, two pair of nylons ending at the clips, no panties,
playing with herself under the light, making little birdlike
sounds of pleasure, while I sat on the floor, my tool
flaccid, gazing into the mirror on the door, watching myself drink with her reflection behind me on the bed, her
fingers moving like crabs in blindness in her hole, playing
up to me. But I was soft.

Early morning. In bed with her. Waking. Seeing the fat
man's face. Rolling over. Fucking her. Getting up. "Go
home, Pauline," my head wracked, the vessels in the brain
aching stretched enough to split like overtightened rubber
bands, "Go home, Pauline," and her saying, "Please let me
stay, please, I gotta stay," and telling her to get the hell
out, grabbing her clothes and shoes and throwing them

out the door, and sending her after; she dressed in her bra and garter belt, she sitting on the hall floor crying, facing me with her crotch aimed at my face, me hurling the fat man's thirty dollars in the air, fluttering around her head. Slamming the door. Ten minutes later, remorse, opening the door. She was gone.

chapter twelve

IN THE spring, Andrew made his Freedom Ride to Richmond. About fifty of us made the trip, even Coretta came
along, dressed in a fluffy white Gone-With-The-Wind
antebellum gown, white stockings, a white parasol gripped
in her white gloved hands, looking like Miss Scarlett
O'Hara really gone to the dogs this time, Rhett Butler
dead and buried, Tara lost for good. We sang on the way
down, Andrew rapping about the expected magnificence
of the whites-only men's room in the depot, about the
marble walls and floors, the wooden toilet seats, the com-
forts and the elegance of the aristocratic South surviving
alone in its non-colored toilets. As he rapped, Sam Parsons
talked about the books he had written, praising most the
ones bombed by the critics, talked about the famous
people he knew and the big, mindbending, fantastic sexual
exploits he had done, the fighters he had fought, the
wars he had won. "I'd give it all up just to be, what?
ah . . . metaphysically, mythically catapulted into history
. . . power's the only road, *political* power, *state* power,
which narrows the legions to me. To be President . . . when

133

I was a kid, I wanted to be President of this wild country. I think I became a writer by default, no default in the gut, but because there was no other way to grab power, to *be* power, not for a Jew anyway, from the Bronx yet, not on a massive scale, not within history. . . ." He was going to write up the Freedom Ride for the *Village Voice,* but all he did was drink and rap about himself and give unasked-for advice and check drunk into a hotel in Richmond. He slept through the demonstration and met us after it was over in a bar and took testimony from us on the success of the mission. It was an easy triumph, that Freedom Ride. It was good. Even Parsons was okay, his talk funny, his phony bully New York attitude a carnival act in the Reb capital.

Took Andrew to the bus station the following day to see him off. We went into the bathroom together. We used the colored one. It was nicer than the whites-only john. Walked to the bus with him in the sunshine down those Richmond streets, him telling me to stay on his side, said there was no other side for decent folks to be on, said it was like the Resistance in France, the Movement was, and to fight the Man and win freedom you had to be standing with your real friends against the Man, the capitalist, against his imperialism, his wars, his racism. That I had to discover, he said, my real friends. I missed him already.

As the bus left the station, he pressed his face against the window. I looked again, and he was gone.

chapter *

BELOW the tracks on 125th Street. Harlem. Two blocks north a dinge queens' baths, on Amsterdam and Lenox, claiming the territory running north and south, the prosperous blacks (the only ones on the street who look like they read *Ebony*), new Willie Lomans pushing King H to the brethren, planting diamond fields in the veins; and the whores and petty hustlers and the shiny pimps in their business suits with unmatched socks, the meat peddlers, working the lousy bars and rooming houses along the American streets Andrew once walked and Malcolm X knew.

A nigger wino—a nigger in the worst, most Southern racist sense ("culturally deprived," as social scientists put it in their hopelessly Official Liberal way, violence internalized, festering, dead men walking)—pissed against the anti-junk signs on a Baptist church near the 125th Street station and, as he did, gave the middle finger up God's ass. SIXTEEN BLACK BOYS KILLED THIS WEEK BY DEVIL JUNK, the sign said. Dead unmourned.

Thursday night, back from a birthday party in Darien

I had been taken to by Mrs. Slugmore, who could not hold her liquor and fell drunk and lost the cock taste she had put out twenty bucks to buy, the party carefully integrated, given in the house of a famous man; warm, lonely, expensive night. Now in the station pissing in the downstairs men's room, where you pay a dime at the top of the stairs to open the steel door and descend, and another dime to shit—railroad capitalism—a dime to stand at the urinal and face a dirty, institution-green wall covered with graffiti and to watch as you leave, the baby-maker done shook dry, a black cock, believe me, a black cock like a marine's swagger stick wagging through the glory hole into the room. Leaving, thinking of Andrew as a kid in an outhouse on his farm reading the Sears' catalogue, sitting on his perch, the bathroom a private place. Private no more.

In the hall where young black kids, denied their city and their names, aliens in their skin, shoot it up the arm and winos lie down to sleep. How pasty white I felt making my way upstairs, the guilt rising with a liberal's reflex, thinking, I too am powerless though responsible. And with it, new to me, the sense that despite my heart and conscience the blacks were not *like* us whites. Unhappy, caught, but unlike us.

On the wall: 8/5/67 8:10 A.M. AM HOT ASSED AND COCKED. 20 YRS. OLD EX-SAILOR, WHITE, WITH GOOD BUILD AND TIGHT HOT WHITE ASSHOLE AND LIKE TO BE FUCKED BY BIG HARD BLACK COCKS—JUST SPENT THE NIGHT WITH MY HUSKY NEGRO TRUCK DRIVER BOY FRIEND—HIS WIFE WAS AWAY SO I SPENT THE NIGHT AND MAN

HOW HE CAN FUCK MY ASS—HE'S 6F2 TALL AND
250 LBS OF REAL HE-MAN MUSCLE WITH A MOST
BEAUTIFUL TEN INCH COCK THAT REALLY
OPENS MY HOT HOLE—HE WON'T USE ANY VASE-
LINE—JUST A LITTLE OF HIS SPIT ON THE TIP
THEN UP GO MY LEGS OVER HIS SHOULDERS
AND HE STARTS TO RAM IT IN AND I SCREAM IN
PAIN BUT HE JUST RAMS IT IN DEEPER UNTIL
I CAN FEEL HIS NICE BLACK ROD HIT MY BELLY
AND HIS BIG BLACK BALLS BOUNCE AGAINST
MY BUNS.

So lily-white that I needed (hoisting four centuries of
memory implacably stuck to the mind like thorns, lynch-
ings at night, chains, blood riots, beatings, deprivations,
sexual crimes, starvation and death without necessity, endless acres harvested and harvested and harvested under a
whip, children wasted) as senators and the President and,
yes, even the white radical leaders and the radical preachers needed, to be skewered by that black cock. Dissolution. That is what they were after. Guilt-ridden, bloated
with collective crime, and it did no good, no good at all,
not after learning of the rumor of Andrew's death somewhere how long ago alone and soundless in some Southern
county unnamed, gone one day, leaving his mother, gone
to meet brothers organizing a nationalist party in South
Carolina, gone and not come back. It did no good for
Andrew or Parker or their living brothers for me to trail
into Darien, a hustler making parlor trade with the meter
running, tripping into town like an assimilated, NAACP-
member, and finding a Token Negress at the party and
propositioning her.

Sunday. I went to St. Mark's-in-the-Bouwerie Episcopal Church to hear an electric rock mass performed by a rock group. I went with a friend of mine named Dan, a pop singer, and with another friend, and we listened as the churchmen went Southern Baptist for one service. Dan thought it was great, wild, man, groovy, like it's too much. He spoke like the early sixties.

A week before the mass I went over to Times Square, the old street hustling camp grounds. I cruised awhile, scored once in Bryant Park. Then I walked up Broadway. I stood on 47th Street near Broadway listening to Rosey preach; Rosey with her mean, weathered, whore's face, her cackle, her vicious *Christian* eyes; Rosey dressed in a white cloak with JESUS SAVES written in silver sequins on the back, throwing Jesus and the Fountain of Emmanuel's Blood at the out-of-town suckers and the deadassed hustlers and the studs on the make, speaking in a Border State accent, one of the Ten self-appointed Righteous left in Sodom. Rosey, on the curb nearly every night, lonely as hell she must have been to put up with the shit up with which she puts, screeching behind her plastic flag, the theatre lights, and signs advertising Castro Convertibles and Calvert booze and Ban-Won't-Wear-Off-As-The-Day-Wears-On throwing light on her sequined clothes: "Sinners, hark! This is the Voice of God speaking ... for He shall come in flaming fire taking vengeance on them that know not God. . . ."

I stood in the crowd and at intervals yelled, "Burn the Witch!" I was there because I was bored, bored with sex, bored with class hustling, with street hustling, bored with my life, and I had seen *Romeo and Juliet* that day and I wanted to fall in love to end the boredom—for love, unlike sex, is never boring—to fall in love as Shakespeare's lovers were in love, as one is in love when one is sixteen and does not appreciate how very long life may be and how very rare love can be. (An actress who was well known and making money and middle aged and famous for her love affairs and who bought hustlers by the dozen and the week, once told me, when she was drunk and lugubrious and groping, that she had been lonely all her life and all her life had been waiting for Someone to come and fill her life and Someone never came.) I enjoyed my loneliness, used to it. It made me feel strong.

Listening to Rosey preach, I noticed a youth, about eighteen years of age, standing on the curb across the street, leaning against a signpost, dressed in white pants and sneakers and a sweater and a thin jacket. Handsome. A black youth, you might know, and I watched him as Rosey cried of God, watched his eyes move over the crowd as he bit his lower lip nervously.

I left and walked up Eighth Avenue to Howard Johnson's. It was about eleven-thirty. The crowds were thick as the theatres closed. I went inside Howard Johnson's and took a booth by the door. I ordered a Coke. I was going to rest a minute and then hit the street again and see if I could score. I was there about ten minutes when the black youth came in and walked by my table and turned around and, seeing me, smiled. Unasked, he sat down at my table across from me, put his elbows on top of the table and held his head in his hands and grinned at me.

He made me nervous, sitting there grinning at me while

I tried to act tough and unself-conscious and keep from smiling back and thought of something hard and un-authentic to say like, fuck off, black boy, something illiberal and effective. But I did not, remember that, I did not send him away. I liked the bastard.

The waitress came over and broke the silence by asking him if he was goin' t'ordah or whetha he was just waitin' for a bus or some damn thing since otha peoples waitin' for the table and this here's no Port Author'ty waitin' room, pal. He ordered, in a Down East accent, indifferent to vowels and r's.

I shook my head. "What the hell you want of me?" I asked . . . direct, in a firm, unemotional voice, a bitch edge to its sound. A hustler's voice, as if I had no idea what he wanted, suspecting he wanted gratis sex, which I was not about to give, my mind preoccupied with Juliet at fourteen or so, dying each night without me. And he was black and I had never made it with a male spade, not even in trade, never certainly as lovers, although I admit the rumble of it was there with Parker, early with Parker.

What did he want? "Nothing. Only want to talk to some-body." He smiled. The *teeth!* Good Christ, the Gold Dust Twins eating watermelon and grinning wide with them teeth.

"About what?" bitchy, I wouldn't give over to his smile. "Don't know . . . just got into New York . . . from Maine . . ." *Colored* in *Maine?* ". . . and I thought . . . been here two days already and I haven't met nobody and I thought I could talk to you since you looked college . . ." shy intonation, eyes lowered, ". . . the city scares me." He had me there, a clamp on the heart, for I, like how many others, was from a place as equally outside history as Maine, and I, too, had been scared. "And I thought maybe we could be buddies." High school in the State of Maine. *Buddies!*

He apologized for following me but he was afraid of queers and of getting mugged (the black middle class, at last) and he did not want to be alone. And *I* looked *safe* to him.

He interested me. Because he was black—that requires no further explanation—and did not seem self-aware of his blackness and because he was young and honest and naïve, and for some reason it was harder all the time to find anyone who was young, honest and naïve. He was charming, with his openness and smile, and he reminded me of boys younger than himself in the Irish and Puerto Rican ghettos in Chelsea, for they were also charming and open, but not naïve.

His name was David. David Cartwright.

"Been to Harlem?" I asked, simply to cut him, but I was bad at cutting, wide of the mark. I wanted him to know that I *knew* he was a black, that is, his being black made him *unlike* me, as Harlem was unlike the Village. That is what I had learned from Andrew. There were many nations within the country, many cities, many tribes.

"I didn't go down to Harlem . . ."

"*Up* to Harlem. Harlem is uptown from here," I corrected him.

". . . up to Harlem. Not yet, only been in town a few days, like I said. What's in Harlem?" Other than blacks, he meant.

Pause, while the waitress unloaded his Coke and pointed out the fifty cent minimum.

"I don't know many black folks," I said, in a very poor Southern accent. "Not anymore."

"I don't either."

"Why not?"

"Not many in Maine, not that I noticed. Aint in my town; my town's small. Not many . . . except for us, I mean."

"Do you feel like a black?" I asked, seeking distance. "Do you *feel* like a black?"

He shrugged. "I don't understand why I should feel different," he said, smiling. I remembered Thelma in South Chicago. Sitting on the window ledge beside her, with her little brother under my arm, and my feeling then, for the first time, white.

I took him downtown to the Village and we went to Max's Kansas City (a circus, Superstars and Company) and to the Ninth Circle (tourists born in New York in the outer boroughs, eating peanuts from barrels and casting the shells to the floor) and to Julius' (where Coretta the Transsexual once stomped with me and Rodney soon after the crown jewels were first dumped into a dustbin), and watched the pretty, wispy, over-delicate, forever young fags cruise each other pleasantly in the bar mirror, hoping that some Luscious Simply Stunning Star or Fantastic Great Playwright would drift in and notice them and carry them—as Jack dreamed of being similarly carried—to the Coast or Broadway; the faggot uglies walking self-consciously to the men's room, flagging hysterically as they passed like gaudy carnival floats, unfollowed. Finally, late, we ended up at an afterhours bar near the Bowery, where Mafia types and black junkies riding high jammed the place. David stayed close, intimidated by the people. And I, drinking too much, felt protective and mellow, the white massah's son taking the house nigger generously on a tour. A cruel image. I was fond of the kid.

Why was he in New York? "My father died, see, a couple years ago and my ma, well, see, she works nights in this county hospital and the house is breaking up, nobody there since my sister run off, with a real bastard, too. And I want to be a painter. I *am* a painter. Inside." Town crowded with wouldbe painters and actors and writers and other assorted artists without a pimp to drum their business and he, a black, wanted to enter the game. "There hasn't been a great Negro painter, none that I know of. So I am going to be it." Before, he had said he did not feel black; by that I think he meant that he felt no anger. "I am going to be famous and rich and everybody's going to want what I paint. I'm going to live a real, beautiful life with a big house and girls and I am going to have a summer place in Maine with about a hundred damn rooms in the house and then I'll be so happy." Like how many other dreamers have I heard, besides myself, spin their future cities in the air. How many? Andrew, Parker, Jack, Willie, Rick, Coretta, on and on.

Yet I understood his dreaming. For his dreaming (his hunger) was where it belonged, in New York, the place to be fed. I, too, wanted that, but in a different way. I missed by a decade going out like Romeo; I would have to settle for something less enchanting: hunger ended.

Like David I wanted that (at a party a while back, several people were talking about a hustler I once knew who was nearly thirty and had given up the streets and taken a job running an elevator; he had been writing poetry for fifteen years or more and he did not write it well, and they said of my friend, he will never be a good poet and he should have died young, for in that way we could mourn him and say, such a promising poet to die so young), but unlike Romeo I was too old to die young.

David drank and rapped about sex and how he got his first chick when he was sixteen (Romeo again) and he spoke without making racial identification, speaking not of "white chicks," or "black (he would say "Negro") chicks," but simply of chicks. He spoke about his life and his broken family and his attempts at sex. He was tied to me in a manner he did not acknowledge by the same centuries-old crimes that tied me to him irrevocably, unbearably. He should have stayed in the State of Maine and forgotten painting and fame. He should not have auctioned his life so cheap.

As he talked about his first girl (fascinated, I wanted to see his penis, just for the record, just to once again deny the myth, in the bar I wanted to see it), as he talked he would smile handsomely, as he talked about sex, smile in an odd way, his mouth smiling more up one side than the other, as if it were not really a smile at all but a distraction, a gesture to take my attention away from his words. He was high and happy . . . buddies . . . in Maine again.

"Come in the john, kid," I said, smiling full.

144

"Why?" Not a hint of suspicion, simply wanting information.

"I want to see your cock."

He looked at me as if I were joking. Then he laughed.

"Come on, David. I want to see how big it is."

He dropped the smile. Disappointment. A dirty request.

"It aint so big," he said, refusing me with such modesty and *youth*—reminding me of Willie on the beach, grinning in the sun, his hair streaked with sunbleach, his teeth glinting in the sun, his eyes green, green, and with *youth,* only with youth able to disarm with the truth inadvertently. With whitey in that: it aint so big.

"No, come on, don't be an ass. I want to see."

He would not meet my eyes.

"You're drunk," he said quietly, his defenses building.

"No, I am not drunk, David."

I stood up and left the table and walked through the bar to the john. Inside. Three urinals. Two booths. Empty. Dim lighting. Foul smell. I leaned against the wall. I *was* high. I watched the ceiling light, a naked bulb hanging at the end of a twisted cord, swing slowly in the breeze from the open window. Cold. I shivered.

I watched the light move and I thought of revolution—the cold air making me feel very Russian—high on booze, there in the head I imagined the blacks winning an impossible revolution. We retreating from the cities into the fields, back, back farther into the caves and hollows, into the languageless darkness, into the penitent night.

In he came, I, resting against the wall, the booze rising, the light seeming brighter now against his dark skin.

145

"Are we buddies?" he asked, using that trite, impossible word, looking at me, my chosen executioner.

"I was in Richmond . . . for civil rights," I said, looking down at the floor, suddenly mortified by my color.

"Buddies?"

"On a Freedom Ride . . . at King's March . . . fought in the streets with my fists against the racists . . . kid, I *worked* for you, before the others . . . I pushed my *ass* for you, kid. . . ."

"Buddies?" he asked, moving closer, extending his hand, touching my shoulder with his hand. I pulled away.

"What are you trying to do to me? What the hell are you trying to do? You're *black!* Understand?" Parker, I thought, I cannot go through it again.

"Let's be buddies."

I pushed away from the wall and shoved past him and went over to the urinal and stood about a foot away so he could get a good look at a real, cut, part Chosen People, proud of it, 100% WHITE cock.

I pissed, shivering as the urine fell, thinking, he threatens me with his openness, he blurs the lines, destroys distinctions, pulls near. Dangerous because it had been so damn long since I had been able to view a black friend with anything other than guilt, because it had been so long since I had been able to be a man, simply, outside of some goddamn cause. In a political age, David was *a*political. How? When I could not even score anymore at a party, anywhere, goddamn it, without sooner or later politics coming up, because of my age, where did I stand, on whose side, forever on whose side did I stand. Didn't he watch the television? What *is* this with no black friends? The kid was some kind of social queer. He didn't know his place, his place being with Andrew, being where Parker would be if, his place was militancy and revolution and the suspicion of *me* as a white boy, too late for love, and hands extended as if there were no Third World, no bloody history, no dead dark friends unseen and soundless, no millions of black humans seeking liberation from a world beyond their height for which I stood, despite my rebellion, in my Snow White skin as token. *He* could extend his hand while I, sunk in his history, could not move toward him except in terms of racial expectations and anguish which he did not admit. He did not act as a black man is expected to act. And where did that leave me— without a part, vulnerable.

After I pissed I turned around to see him standing staring down at the floor, his fly open, a limp cock hanging out of his white pants, black against the bright white cloth.

"It aint so big," he said.

It was early morning when we got to his room at the Manhattan Hotel, still clean of each other, wary now, the liquor wearing thin, the dawn up; and he lay on the double bed, his black skin moist, his wet hair shiny in the light on the fake satin quilt like sunlight on water, his brown eyes shiny and clear, his forehead dotted by tiny beads of sweat. We were both uptight, cautious, tense. I liked him very much.

I stood near the door several feet from the bed. I could think of nothing to say. He lay watching me. Finally:

147

"What do you think of Martin Luther King's assassination?"

He laughed. It was an absurd question.

"What do *you* think?" he replied, wanting to be coached.

"I think it was shit," I said.

"So do I."

That settled, he asked me if I would see him tomorrow. I shrugged. Then, in a small voice, "Come and sit on the bed."

"Why?" I asked, suspicious.

"So we can talk."

"We can talk like this." I was sober. No fag play.

"No, please," he said. I hesitated. He asked again. I went and sat down on the bed by him because I wanted to and because I knew if I did not he would not ask me again.

"Do you like me?" he asked, meaning did I love him.

"Yeah, I like you," meaning only that.

He smiled and sat up and reached out and touched my hair, taking a strand of it between the tips of his fingers and rolling it, feeling the texture of it as if he were a buyer of thread.

"You like me very much?"

"Yeah, I guess I do."

I stood up and went to the door. It seemed very warm in the room. "I'm leaving, kid."

"Why?"

"Got to get home."

"Why?"

"Because I do."

"We'll get together tomorrow?"

148

"Sure, why not?" Now it was my turn to smile. I was leaving, the kid putting me up-close and I was getting out. I would not see him again. I could not afford to spend my life comforting one lonely Uncle Tom teenager kid after another, one scared, apolitical, causeless, black/white boy time and again. There were worse problems than his and he belonged to us no more. The integrationist game was done with, killed for me in Andrew's deathly silence, no more the playing of roles scripted by UNICEF cards . . . BROTHERHOOD OF MAN . . . the One World At Peace Day was gone. He was black, whether he ached with it or not, and he did not need *me* as a *black* man, not this hustling white loser. He needed his own. Picket, burn, fight, revolt, and he would have me but I was not there to gentleness, simplicity, nor to ease. Not anymore. My debt, which he did not acknowledge, was too great for me, whether he admitted it or not, too vastly precious for me to relinquish for us to be buddies in the good old State of Maine high school pep fest sense. It was too late for fraternity outside of Andrew's Movement, woefully too late for love.

I stood by the door observing him lying handsome on the smooth, green spread. I opened the door. He came up to me. He was shorter than me and he was grinning at the promise. The door was open, a draft was coming in from the hall, and he put his hand on my shoulder (in Richmond, Andrew left me at the Trailways bus depot where he was to catch a bus to South Carolina to go home and fight in the Movement, to take up arms, he said, just like the white folks' law allows, to defend his friends; and at the station, in front of a line of Southern whites standing behind us waiting to board the bus, he stood on the step of the bus and reached over and placed his hand on my shoulder just before he climbed aboard and leaned over and kissed my mouth . . . and I felt threatened by the whites in his public kiss) and leaned toward my face to kiss me good-bye. I pulled away abruptly and laughed. My movement caught him off balance and he stepped forward to right himself and I shoved him back with my hand. He fell. It was like pushing a little kid. I laughed.

On the wall: I NEVER DID NOTHING UNTIL TWO MONTHS AGO WHEN MY COUSIN BROUGHT HIS COLORED FRIEND FROM THE NAVY—21—HE WAS ON LEAVE AND VERY HANDSOME 6' MUSCULAR WITH SOFT BLACK HAIR HE ASKED ME IF I WANTED TO GO FOR A DRIVE WITH HIM & I WENT HE STOPPED THE CAR IN A DARK QUIET SPOT AND HUGGED ME BUT I FOUGHT THEN HE KISSED ME ON THE LIPS AND I GAVE IN WE STOPPED & HE LAY WITH ME IN THE BACK SEAT HE LET ME SUCK HIS HOT THICK BLACK COCK AND SUCKED MY HOT FRESH ONE THEN HE GOT ON TOP OF ME & FORCED HIS COCK UP MY VIRGIN ASS AND HE SHOT A HOT WAD INTO ME THEN HE TURNED ME OVER AND LET ME RAM MY WHITE PRICK UP HIS ASS WE KISSED AND KISSED EACH OTHERS BODY THE NEXT DAY WE WENT FOR A TRIP TO A MOTEL IN JERSEY WHERE WE WENT TO BED TOGETHER AND MADE LOVE FOR A WHOLE DAY BEFORE HE LEFT ME HE INTRODUCED ME TO A YOUNG BLACK FRIEND

OF HIS AND WE ARE NOW LOVERS HES JUST
GREAT AND MY HOT SEX DRIVES ARE SATISFIED
FOR NOW—HOWEVER IF ANY *YOUNG NICE* MAN
OR *BOY* WANTS TO MEET ME OVER THE XMAS
VACATION CALL 288————ANY EVENING EXCEPT
WED DEC 28 AND ASK FOR TEDDY PREFERABLY
BEFORE DEC 28.

At the electric rock mass, with Dan singing along next
to me in the pew . . . *we are here because we are men, but
we deny our humanity. We are stubborn fools and liars
to ourselves. We do not love others. We war against life.
We hurt each other. We are sorry for it and we are sick
from it. We seek new life . . . Lord have mercy upon us. . . .*
I thought of the black youth, David, and I envied him
because his causelessness abrogated entirely the hunger
for dissolution felt by me. Not in history, free of it. And
me? But maybe for me death, violence, was where the life
lay. I was pulled toward it, toward that and shame, layered
like concrete on my back. To desire to be taken as a race
beyond the point of no return. Perhaps that sensibility was
not in fact contemporary, more liberal than revolutionary,
for I was *not* remorseless as most pimps and crackers and
preachers and revolutionary frauds were. Remorseless. In
the church with Dan, in the beat and thumping chorus,
in the lilting *Lord Have Mercy Upon Us . . . I Am Not
Worthy,* it came again, a nostalgia for death, the nostalgia
experienced on the ferry, nameless (that, for me, defined
the resurrected Christ, dripping like a French whore with
the stench of murder), and dissolution in the beat. And I
resented the impropriety of kids breaking into the aisles

151

after communion and dancing, white and black, as young as Cartwright, dancing together. That was obscene, *life,* friend, bursting into the celebration of the remembrance of his death. His DEATH. Pretty final, from what I can determine from the state of things.

In the morning David should smile for he was stronger than me, even standing in the doorway of the hotel room, his hair lovely soft and glistening in the light, looking tired and beat out and wounded, reminding me of a young boy fieldhand in the Deep South at night walking through the dark yellow pasture to his shack, his shirt pulled above his belly, his body in a tired slouch, a thin, barely discernible line of black down running along the flat face of his stomach. Standing in the doorway he was stronger than me. I missed him, his strength, full of him, empty. Lord, wanting to see his queer smile again and hear him talk to me, to taste his strength.

chapter fourteen

I CALLED David Cartwright at his hotel. A week had passed, and he had checked out, leaving no forwarding address. I was disappointed, in a sense, for I was anxious to see him and yet wary of it (I walked by Howard Johnson's at night, on the chance of catching sight of him, and asked for him at the bars we had hit hoping he had returned, for I was lonely for him, and I knew it was wrong to have left him as I did—as I knew I could not have left him any other way, unless I was willing to cross to the other side of the street and walk it like a perv. That I could not do) and I felt guilty for having treated him like a jocker when maybe that had not been in him, and I also felt bad because he was really set up for a bummer in New York City, being naïve as he was, without a friend. He must have run back to the State of Maine. Better that way.

On an impulse (because of Cartwright and what he reminded me of, and because he made me miss Willie, too—didn't everything? Man, didn't everything?) I phoned the Rector in Chelsea, whom I had worked for, thinking I could acquire information on Willie. The Rector invited me down to dinner the following night.

We had beef stew, the family and me. It was like coming home after you had left for good, gone and made your way in the world and coming home was good because you were equal to it, you knew you did not have to stay.

The Rector and his wife had not changed, they looked the same as before to me, he slightly more gray but still essentially the same. The baby had grown, now was walking and jabbering (I wore an Australian bush hat that night, with a wide brim, one edge of it snapped to the crown, and I threw the hat on a chair and the baby grabbed it and waddled around with it on, and then pulled it off and held it, nibbling on the rim of it; the baby sat in a highchair across from me at the dinner table and played with the food, and the baby reminded me of sister Lily the first night we arrived at auntie's boardinghouse, seated on a pile of books at the table).

The Rector asked me what I was doing, was I still working as a clerk? I was confused, not wanting to tell him, so I was vague about it. "What are you going to do in the future?" he asked.

"Don't know. I keep being asked that, and I don't know." He remarked that being asked about the future was the price of being young. He did not press me further.

After dinner we went into the living room and the Rector made us gin and tonics; his wife opened the French doors onto the yard and the wind blew in and it was like that summer again, and through the open door I could hear people laughing and arguing in the tenements be-

yond the yard, Spanish and rock music echoing across the
back fences, dogs barking.

I asked about the boys I had worked with, about Rick
and Juan and Dave and Willie.

"Rick is in school. In college. He's a freshman at the
City College," he replied, obviously proud of Rick, that
one success out of a thousand failures making it seem
worthwhile, the faith and the labor.

"He wants to be a politician. Can you imagine!" his
wife said, laughing.

"Look at Kennedy's father, or grandfather. Which one
was mayor of Boston?"

"The grandfather," his wife said.

"Well, his background, his early life was more . . . was
more disadvantaged than Rick's. Look at him."

"And Willie?" I asked, my stomach tight, expecting the
worst.

"I don't really know," he said, "The family moved out
of the neighborhood about a year ago. I don't see his
mother anymore. Poor woman. I think they live uptown
now, somewhere. . . ."

"Willie works on the docks," his wife interrupted,
"That's what I heard at least. I think he's a longshoreman,
or an apprentice. Something to do with boats."

After a time I mentioned their son Peter, told them
that he had been in New York several times in the past
year, that I had gone drinking with him on occasion and
that I thought he was a good kid.

"Isn't that odd," the Rector said. "He never mentioned
you to us."

"Perhaps he forgot. He's like that," his wife said. But

what was there for him to mention? That we got plowed together and chased girls and bought a couple of prosties, that I had, let's be honest, for the bread procured whores for him and his friends from the Point? What was worth mentioning in that to your old lady?

"He'll be graduating soon. Why don't you go up and see him, you can go with us?"

"Maybe," I said, knowing that I would. I had never seen the Point or any kind of graduation and I was intrigued.

When I left I walked out on 20th Street. In front of PS 6, where Willie and his buddies had jumped me, there were about fifteen boys playing horse-and-rider against the wall. I didn't recognize any of them.

In June I spoke to the Rector and he again suggested that I go up to West Point for graduation. I telephoned Peter. He asked me to come up the day before. I decided to go.

West Point. Basket Days. I arrived in the late afternoon on a bus from New York City—pink beads around my neck, white bell bottoms, a navy blouse (I looked like a sailor), and a SCREW WAR button on my collar— and met Peter in the lounge of the hotel at the Academy. A nice hotel, pseudo-Tudor decor inside, baronial like a men's club or hunting lodge, like an old-fashioned resort in the Catskills.

The weather was warm and clear and we sat in the cafeteria of the hotel drinking Cokes (it was off-limits to liquor), the place empty except for a few cadets and their families grouped around tables talking. It seemed like Visitors' Day at a prison. Peter was dressed in a gray uni-

156

form, the trousers tight around his ass and basket, the jacket undone in front, sweating, his face flushed, looking healthy and inordinately clean, Middle American, his hair clipped army short, his face shiny and well scrubbed. He spoke about his four-year hitch at the Point, which he had hated at first, wanting to run away, then becoming resigned to it, and ultimately learning to enjoy it as he moved up the ranks and became a model soldier. A 100% All-American Patriotic Gentleman and Warrior, U.S. Government property all the way. Proud of his country's wars and his faith in Pax Americana and Fortress Taiwan.

In the morning Peter would be graduated and commissioned and given a month's furlough before the army sent him to a Special Forces camp to learn counterinsurgency warfare. In the end he would be shipped to what he termed, without conscious irony, "Freedom's war." Over there.

Peter was at West Point because as the son of a clergyman he was able to win a scholarship to an Episcopal military academy, and because he was bright in mathematics, and because, most importantly, the commandant of the school was a graduate of West Point who got hung up on Peter's sandy blond hair, his eyes, his strength, his refusal to express emotion (in Peter's taut insistence on guarding himself emotionally, as if his survival depended upon it, in that discipline of feeling, he was like a winning hustler). West Point material was right. At the Point, Peter bent completely away from his parents, into a narrow and polished corridor of attitudes and conventions, and an elitism that took joy at the idea of barking orders and going to fight in the jungle. Peter, Episcopalian, Republican, desiring to rid the world of Reds and protesters and long-haired radicals and other American anathemas; Peter who thought the dead Kennedys invidious and peace senators creeps and most of the Supreme Court eminently impeachable.

Peter, three of his classmates and myself, the winter before, had gone over to the West Side in Manhattan, after having hit the singles bars on First and Second Avenues, the five of us playing it like sailors on leave, playing reckless and filled with a sense of life, vigor, and we ended on 72nd Street at the apartment of a girl one of the cadets knew (apparently the entire academy knew of her, she acted as a kind of service station for tourist cadets). I cannot remember her name, but I do remember that she was a model who advertised in the *East Village Other* and ran a mail order business selling pictures of herself ("Ten female anatomical studies for ten dollars. Satisfaction guaranteed.") and possessed breasts which looked quite literally like flesh-colored honeydew melons. She was a very intelligent girl who loved to have young men around. Her only bad feature was her face. Unattractive, to be kind. Maybe that's why she did it freebee. She loved young men, or, more precisely, sex with young men and she took it standing and sitting and bending over and lying down and loved doing it, could eat a peach, or watch the television, and not miss a grind. And she was a match for Peter in the art of emotional distancing.

The girl (I am saying girl; she was in her late twenties) played a game with us by making us pay for her by signing a letter to the President. We signed false names. I signed Cecil Rhodes. I think Peter signed Cardinal Cushing. What the letter said was this: DEAR SIR, MENE MENE TEKEL UPHARSIN.

Translated that reads,

GOD HAS NUMBERED YOUR EMPIRE,
AND FINISHED IT.
YOU ARE WEIGHED IN THE BALANCES,
AND FOUND WANTING.
YOUR EMPIRE IS DIVIDED,
AND GIVEN TO THE MEDES AND PERSIANS.

As we talked in the cafeteria, Peter laughed when he remembered the evening and the letter. He said the girl had been invited to graduation on condition that she carry a placard with the MENE MENE etc. written on it. He thought it was a funny idea.

There was one other peculiarity about that evening in the winter, something I never mentioned to Peter but which bothered me. When we fucked her (two of the cadets refused) each of us took her in turn while the others stood and watched. Said nothing, simply stood and stared. Like people at a construction site. Later, when I took a piss, Peter came into the bathroom and stood at the bowl with me and took out his cock and watched me piss. And then he pissed. What interested me was that there was something about that episode which was characteristic of the cadets in general and which reminded me of S&M queens who, in turn, remind me of pre-adolescent boys. All talk a lot about excrement, are deeply interested in each other's genitals, and in displaying themselves in front of one another with obviously studied casualness, and they like public sex, doing it one after another in front of the others, like a bikeboy club in a

159

gangbang. And they share an interest in pain and combat, in leather and guns, in regimentation and super-masculinity, in physicality and discipline.

Later that night, Peter sneaked me into the barracks, gray stone, bleak decor, immaculate and bare as monastic cells, smelling of leather and oil and sweat and disinfectant, and he pulled out a bottle of Old Crow and called in four fellow seniors, and we sat together in the half-light of his suite, one civilian and five cadet officers puffed with rank—it was insufferably muggy and hot in the room, three of the fellows in white shorts, one naked, lovely, seated on the bureau with one foot resting on an open drawer, the other kicking absentmindedly against the wall of the bureau, his legs spread open to us—and drank whiskey and rapped, swearing a lot.

The cadet officers were certain of many things: the nation was going socialist, the army lost wars because the politicians tied their hands behind their backs, soon it would be too late. *Who will save the country?* The answer was sitting in the room with its legs spread, and sleeping in the other barracks, and housed, itching and impatient, in forts and camps and recruiting shacks and officer clubs and general staff offices. Odd, I could picture auntie's nightmare of the International Jewish Conspiracy seeping across their Real American military minds, that myth of Jew Power which little Americans comfort themselves with when the rent is due—the Jews and the commies, the Jews and the International Bankers, the Jews and the upstartin' nigras. It is said that Army men measure a soldier's loyalty by the length of his foreskin. Peter's was cut, poor bastard.

I sat on the bunk next to Peter. We talked about his parents, and how he was hurt because his father refused to come to the Point for graduation because he could not bear anything to do with war—his father was passionately pacifist.

We discussed the times we had hit it off together in Manhattan, he and his friends swaggering down the street in their cadet uniforms, tiny waists, broad shoulders, tight in crotch and ass, and loving to walk like cruising sisters, chicken meat/government inspected, playing cock-tease to the basketeers along Greenwich Avenue and Third Avenue, making lonely gays ache at the passing of untouchable trophies.

We talked awhile and then Peter, by way of diversion —he was feeling high and I was on his turf and I think he wanted to impress me with privilege—ordered the floor cadet to come double-time into the room (the floor cadet: a plebe terrified of senior officers, frantic to make it through the few days remaining in the school year without fucking up his future—YOU HAVE A FUTURE IN THE ARMY! beginning and ending every sentence with "Sir!" and speaking as if the words themselves were painful in their danger). The kid, aroused and taken from sleep, maybe seventeen or eighteen years old, stumbled into the room and stood at attention in his boxer shorts—his cock half-erect from sleep, making him self-conscious and vulnerable as he stood rigidly, silently, his head held high and back, eyes staring blankly forward.

The cadet officers examined him severely, Peter glancing over at me, enjoying himself. "Been playing with yourself, Masters?"

"No, Suh!" Southern. They never learn.

"Masters is the pansy in his platoon," Peter remarked, turning to me. "Aren't you, Masters?" Peter was playing at command, in rehearsal for bigger things. His voice was rough. I think he was nervous.

"Yes, Suh!" the boy answered, bewildered, his face red. I believed him.

"Boy, you are going to shine my shoes. You are going to shine them until they glow, Buster!" The command, a little forced, a trifle unsure. Peter was overdoing it.

Peter sat on the bunk next to me, winking confidentially. "Reminds me of boarding school," he said. I shook my head. It made no human sense. I smoked a cigarette and felt sorry for the plebe, or perhaps more embarrassed for him than sorry, as he knelt before Peter, back impossibly straight, as Peter pulled on his dress shoes and rested his feet high on the boy's thighs while Masters polished away. Erotic, in a perverse manner, the kid working hard over the leather, a short lock of hair falling over his forehead as his arms moved furiously, his forehead beaded with sweat, polish staining his skin; Peter observed the work coolly, detached, snapping out an occasional order, "More polish! Harder, Buster!" as detached as I had been in Bryant Park the first time my skin was bought . . . the other cadet officers talking among themselves, making small jokes . . . the boy's sandy blond head bobbing between the officer's legs as he spat and brushed.

The shine complete, Peter pushed Masters roughly away with his foot and laughed to break the tension—the room was quiet now, I was embarrassed for them both, and I think the sexuality of the situation became obvious even to Peter, for he said gruffly, mannishly, "He'd suck an officer if it'd mean a stripe, wouldn't you Masters?"

The kid looked at me on the bed, counting me as one of them, and then glanced at Peter, looking directly at him, the muscles at the back of the boy's jaw twitching. He hated us both. "Yes, Suh!" he said, very loudly, "*Any*-time you want, Suh!"

The following morning I arranged to catch a ride back to New York at noon. I watched the parade of cadets in dress whites, some with baskets *too* grand showing through the cloth. Laundry. I heard the Chief of Staff address the graduating class about Standing Firm in the world, etc. And I watched the cadets throw their hats into the sky into the sunshine, the cadets giving forth with enormous shouts of triumph and delight. They had come of age.

Peter and his mother met me in the lobby of the hotel and told me there was to be a cocktail party in an hour, would I come? I declined. I felt out of place, I found the atmosphere false and potentially threatening. It was all, the uniforms, the clipped, overused manners, the unbear-able correctness and stiffness of these young men, the feigned, militant, butch, killing-on-orders attitude, the pride of it, all foreign to what I knew. Much worse, phonier, more deadly.

I went downstairs to the men's room. There were several cadets inside, with their jackets off, washing their faces, brushing back their hair, high and happy. I pissed and went inside a stall and took toilet paper to blow my nose. Cut through the partition between the stalls was a glory hole, and above it was written, "I LIKE BIG COCK," and "THE ARMY FUCKS SEA PUSSY." A glory hole.

chapter fifteen

"WHERE you been?" Sam Parsons asked, drunk again, always drunk or hung over or on his way into a bender, "Where *have* you been?" slapping me enthusiastically on the shoulder, like buddies in the State of Maine, and then sliding in beside me in the booth, his girl friend standing and watching for a minute, finally settling for the bench opposite us, smiling at Sam good-humoredly, as if she was used to tolerating much worse.

"Barbara," Sam began, beaming, squinting at her, "I want you to meet . . . " trailing off into laughter, forgetting my name. I introduced myself to her. "Old friend, *very* old friend of mine, yes he is," squeezing my arm to compensate for losing my name, "And I do wonder where he has been. Shacked up with some rich broad, I bet."

"Where have I been? Since when, Sam?" I asked, delighted, and working to remember when I had last seen him. It had been sometime after the Fall of Richmond, in a saloon or party, somewhere vague and hot, for the only thing definite I could recall was the image of Sam crouching in a high-backed Victorian chair in a large room filled with giddy people and he, in dead earnest, acting as if he had a machine gun in his hand, blasting the room with bursts of lead, like a small boy fighting Indians, shouting, *"rat-ta-tat-tat . . . got you, bugger! bang! and you, bastard! bang! bang!"* with the guests joining in the game and falling playfully before his gun, the carpets stacked with giggling corpses, the party degenerating into a playground rout with people hurling scotch-bottle bombs and drink-filled glasses and, in the end, lamps and ashtrays at each other's chair-forts—Sam, with his curly hair trembling and his eyes much too fierce, the game real; Sam crying somewhere, at some other scene, in the winter, outside, I remember, upstairs in the loft of an underground film-maker where we went to see a film which was banned in the United States, tinsel types, flute blowers, climbers, and Sam lugubrious and foulmouthed; that was the last time, that winter, after the film had begun he stomped out and later I climbed down six flights of stairs and out into the snow to find him sitting without a coat in a snow-bank weeping; I helped Sam into a taxi and he said, absurdly, in a stage whisper, in a phony British accent, a bad imitation of Basil Rathbone, "I stand in terror before your ululation, and before your grief I am mute," which meant absolutely nothing to either me or Sam, but he declared it anyway, with great force. And once I was with him when he was, from what I could perceive, cold sober, in a nasty snit about his wife, Sybil devouring through her illimitable cavity, emasculating him, absorbing, like blood absorbs sugar, his ambition with his sperm. Or words to that effect.

"So where were you?" Sam asked again, and it occurred

166

to me that, by God, Parsons was actually interested in what I had been doing. "I went to West Point for the graduation." I thought that would intrigue him. It did.

"What?" he said, "That's trade territory, is it? Market fallen in New York, now you got to go upstate to the boys' camp to score?"

I looked at him a moment, not knowing whether he was serious and I should be pissed. "You dumb, Sam? I went up for the graduation of a friend, the son of a preacher I know."

"Some friend. Militarist swine." He glanced over to Barbara and repeated, "Militarist swine," she nodded in agreement, and then Sam went into his standard tirade against the army. And he spoke with the identical intensity he employed against his wife, the hatred deeply felt yet somehow unconvincing because its object was too familiar to him, what he hated he loved . . . the night he went into his bitch against his wife, that night he said to me, and when I heard him I thought the man was unraveling . . . *ball her tonight, stud, I'll tell you what she digs, God, do I know what that bitch digs! tonight you ball my wife for me, be a friend, you ball that, that dyke, you know that, you know she beds other women, goddamn, do you know that, lezzies . . . God, she must hate me. . . ."* I thought I had reached the other edge, madness rampant, this was it. And it was tough to watch, Sam when he went into his word fits and the words caked with mean shit, like poison leaking through cracks in his skull into his brain, nothing I could ever see triggering Sam off. Christ, I tell you, when I thought about Sam I used to wonder why anybody with that much money and brains and fame could be as fucked up as street jocks, the poor with their parts broken and irreplaceable. Careening like a suicidal drunk along the ledge of a skyscraper and never quite losing balance, pounding on, driven by and possessed by a massive, illogical, inexplicable energy, like some wild Model T in a Sennett comedy, which plows through fields, barns, crowds, knocks through brick walls and tumbles off cliffs and chugs on through rivers and forest fires and arrives at its destination puffing, without tires or fenders or hood, utterly denuded, and backfires loudly, farting, eager to roar on. Sam was like a Mack Sennett prop, an impossible machine set in motion and gone bananas which cannot be stopped, and drives on wanting to be stopped. In its craziness is its charm. Sam was like that, he made madness and suffering look *good*. And that's bad.

"We're flying up to Newport tonight," Sam boasted, glancing at Barbara, checking with her eyes. Going to Newport was news to her. "Ever been to Newport, stud?" He leaned over against me when he asked, and I knew he hoped I had never been there, wanting to surprise me with the place.

"Nope," I did not even know where it was, except that it was on a beach and the rich lived there and sailed boats on its water.

"Goddamn!" He was delighted. A new game. "To Newport!" he said, and stood very dramatically, lifting his glass high in his hand. He paused and stared at me. I caught on fast. I grabbed my drink, and then Barbara stood and the three of us, like Russian guardsmen saluting the Czar, raised our glasses to Newport and sent them crashing against the floor.

Oceanside, on the beach at Newport late at night. Sam Parsons lay on the sand with Barbara beside him asleep with her head resting on his chest below the hollow of his throat, her face inclined toward me. Sam, flat out, with his mountainous chest and mountainous belly and ruddy legs. The Beauty and the Beast, her body too lovely, perfect—the profile of her face: large black eyes, full, sensual lips, the bottom lip turned downward and curled, her nose, incredibly WASP, straight, small, exquisitely sculptured, the nostrils delicate. Beautiful she was, robust and healthy in a suburban country club way (always I see her standing in the sunshine on a court in Newport, holding a racket in her hand and yelling at Sam to get up off the ground and serve) resembling in her energy Sam's wife, but younger and more at ease with men (for she *liked* men, and that, in my experience, was rare among American women) her body as yet unspread by pregnancy.

The reason Parsons brought her along that weekend had not to do with love, but with symbols. He was afraid of his wife. Many men are who sense that their wives do not take them seriously as men, who divvy out praise in thimbles and deny them what they claim as triumph in life. Ten years he lived under the brunt of her attacks against his admittedly hypermasculine pose, against his middle age. Barbara, unlike his wife, did not have the talent for wounding Sam in his manhood (his wife, I think, suspected Sam of skirting on the tinsel edges of gaydom. Certainly Sam's fondness for me, a hustler, and for boxers and pro football players and even truckers, all practitioners of the Superbutch, reinforced her suspicion). Barbara respected his work. She gave Sam something he needed badly...youth and ardor and indiscriminate praise. Only she could call Sam "America's greatest living writer," and have Sam appear to believe it. She was WASP, there lay the symbolism, and her race was carved beyond dispute across her face.

Sam lay beside her, I on the other side. I thought about Parsons, that weekend, for the first time, really learning about his work and life, his fighting in the Pacific during the Second World War and making a best-selling book about his war experience. Sam referred to the war a lot. The war was never over for him. It was housed in some dead bag sewed inside his chest and slowly its corruption seeped into his veins decaying his soul. "The first time I ever killed a man, shot him...he was a straggler I came across on patrol, young, he was lost, and we studied each other a moment and then I raised my rifle and shot him. He never moved. Not once did he move. He looked surprised, really, when it hit him. As if I had violated some rule. When I went to sleep that night, I slept like a top. When I woke the morning was still dark and it took me a while to gather my thoughts. I had forgotten I was in war. And I remembered it, with a kind of dawning dread, that it was true. No dream. That it was true. I feel that, wakening into dread, I feel it often." In his books and in his talk he drummed up the past, and I thought, Sam, you're in the wrong business, you should have gone into business in the Bronx, peddled fish, Sam, you should have been a shopkeeper where you would not have to explain yourself in print; you should have dealt in mathematical abstractions, computing figures on soup cans, and married some WASP-nose, pliable, unliberated woman (married Barbara) and sired equally WASP-nosed kids. But instead, for Sam the war never knew its peace and passed without hiatus into Korea and flowed unresisted and inexorably into Vietnam, providing not the time for wounds to close, crimes to be distanced.

I lay on the other side of Barbara, not touching her but near enough to catch the heat from her body when the wind died momentarily, and when it lifted to carry in the breeze the scent of lilac from her hair to me. Cloudless night, the moon high, tiny in the sky, its light on the water stretching unbroken on the waves, sparkling on the wet sand near the tidal line as the sea fell back in intervals after crashing on the shore. Warm night and lilac and the three of us naked, Parson's hair and mine wet from skinny dipping in the ocean. Peaceful. My body trembled slightly from pushing into Barbara after he was through grunting like an ox in his sex, his sperm inside and mine to follow and she whimpering on the beach, *"oh, hon, hon . . ."* the threesome tired. Sam snoring, and me? Well, I was thinking it was time to pull the life together, not a kid anymore and my body would be giving way in time and I did not have Sam's fame or money, I did not have community or purpose, I had nothing to protect me from the crunch. I could see myself being shoved into a corner, ending up a busted whore like my old man and, God help me, maybe even drawing in the lot an encounter like I gave one fat man on the Seamen's roof (for maybe what I pitied in him, and there was pity there, was what I saw of my future mangled in him) and, too, I thought of the ferry ride with Pauline and shivering on the deck from what I was beginning to recognize—there was an urge to violence in me, maybe to dying, and it was in some confused distortion interrelated to my sexuality, to the uses to which I put my sex. Man, it was strange the way violence was welded in my experience to the people I was hung on, Parker and Doris and Thelma and Andrew and, in a sense, Willie. All that together was the network of my manhood, or lack of it, the bits and pieces of reality that I collected in growing up. It seemed to me that the most real thing in life was death. It was the only thing that was concrete, definite, that was hard and immutable and could be counted on. And violence had a shadow of that reality to it (and was therefore somehow more *real* than life without violence) for it carried the crisp promise of death. Like a rat carries an epidemic.

I thought a great deal that weekend, with Sam I had room to think. I decided to get the hell out of New York. Soon. I did not know where I would go, but I knew I had to leave. I was a dead-ender in Manhattan. I was on a wheel turning ever in the same yard. All my life, you understand, *all my life* I felt cornered, even as a kid, all my fucking life I felt trapped and wary, having to lash out, to stay on the attack. Not to sleep. Man, not to chance a bummer for anything. Backed into a corner, with my fists up and striking out. World, keep your distance.

I decided to run from New York. Even if I were rich, I think I would have wanted to run from New York. Even if I were Sam Parsons The Writer I would run, for look at Sam The Man who stayed too long somewhere with a gun. Sam The Bloody Man ... consider: in his war he stood in a field and at a distance of ten yards shot down, in the blinding sunlight, two women and a man, suspected collaborators (aren't they all, everyone with slant eyes and darker skins, aren't they all suspect and expendable, all collaborators with the enemy) murdered them cold in daylight and watched them fall and walked across the field, his goddamn rifle in his hand, and kicked the bodies and when one moved exploded with a shot a human head ... he did that (or that was done to him) and was able to talk about it, *write* about it as if the doing was a Boy Scout merit badge, as if it *proved* something beyond the fact that he was a murderer, and worse, for Sam to *miss* it, to desire to face the fucking act next time more equally (the next time never coming, unless it came dimly perceived in bar brawls) the odds not quite as unbalanced. Sam. Too old to retrace his life, reprieve denied him. What followed was a slow pacing out of an end.

Barbara was asleep. We had smoked grass and then we fucked and now we were tired on the beach.

"Beautiful night, Sam. Aint it one beautiful night?" I reached above Barbara's head and tapped Sam awake.

"Aint what?" awake and distracted, gazing at the moon.

"The night," I said. I sat up and looked out at the water, the waves low, the moonlight skimming on top, cresting the water. "Beautiful," I said, remembering Lake Michigan in the summer. I glanced over at Sam. The light shone on his body and on Barbara's. She was over on her side, facing him, one leg lifted and fallen against his thigh, the hair of her sex visible in the moonlight. I remembered the soft feel of it in my hands.

Sam smiled up at me. I lay back again. "Got to begin thinking about your future, stud," Sam said, "Retirement from trade, that aint far off, you know that?" Sam was playing Father, his voice weighted with concern. Sam had three basic roles. They were Writer-Celebrity, and Father ("Not forever can you go stumbling around those mean streets," he'd say) and Tough Kid (the bar fights and booze and dirty words with the fake proletarian accent, the disruption and the capacity to gather around himself a coterie of butch types in a private gang to hunt Manhattan together. And, in this role, his deep anti-faggot feelings would come rumbling out, for he looked on homosexuals much as hustlers did: they were *queer* and that made them fearsome). "I aint suggesting that you get a job, but you ought to learn a craft . . ."

"I got one."

". . . a real craft, like carpentry or acting. Just in case."

"In case what?"

"Age, stud."

"Man," I said, putting him down, "Where's your guts?" But it scared me, having no insurance against it. I did not want to lose, and I thought I probably would because I believed that something broke you down in the end. I knew it was not the System, as Parker and Andrew claimed. It was wider than that. Not as wide as auntie's LIFE, but almost.

Sam lay thinking, and for a long time he did not say anything. Then he turned to me and began: "About when I was your age. In the war, many of my buddies got it in the war. It wasn't all paths of glory as in my book." I had never read his book, but I disliked his talk of war, it was decades ago, before I was born. "And we killed many Japs. Tortured some. Cigarette butts under their balls, on their thighs." He laughed, the confession over,

174

the war still naked but not dead, and swung to his feet and grabbed my ears and pulled them playfully as he stood over me, his belly protruding, middle aged but looking younger in the nude, looking like a fat, squat Jewish kid I knew in fifth grade, a grind.

A few weeks later I met Barbara in the Village. We had coffee together in an outdoor cafe on Bleecker Street.

"Where's Sam?" I asked, surprised he wasn't with her. When she asked me to meet her, I assumed she was asking for Sam.

"Home, I think. He's working on a new book. About the war. A novel. I don't see what it has to do with the war. The war isn't even mentioned in it." She glanced away from me out to the street. We were both silent. She thought a moment. Then she looked at me, trying to control her voice as she spoke. "He isn't altogether well. The War thing, I guess . . . I don't know . . . he's a beautiful . . . a gentle man, but he isn't really well."

"Who is?" I asked, envious of her concern and feeling sorry for her. All she was into was Sam Parsons, that was what she lived for and if you did not like Sam Parsons, if he did not interest you, then it was a drag being with Barbara for what she rapped about constantly was him.

"He's been getting into fights, and he can't fight well. . . ." She said it in a rush, as if it were some deadly secret. It wasn't news to me.

"Maybe that's what he needs," I said, honestly believing that he and a hell of a lot of other people were pushing hard and hungry into one kind of leather/lavender nightmare or another, moving into Camp Pain.

Easy to do. I was tempted by it. But it was the wrong thing to say.

"God, no!" she laughed falsely. Her eyes were scared. It was on her mind, as she laughed with her hair falling over her shoulders, thin throat long and lovely and laughing, it was what she dreaded to admit.

That was in September. In October of that year, Sam Parsons brought his war home.

Barbara telephoned me late, around three o'clock in the morning, and in a thick whisper, hysterical, begged me to come to her apartment at once, whispering with Parsons shouting drunkenly in the background, "You filthy slut! I'll murder you!"

I dressed quickly, resenting Barbara for calling me at such a goddamn hour and hating Parsons for being on an unending binge. Tired. I was tired from putting up and out that night. I needed my sleep.

I took a taxi to Yorkville where Barbara lived. When I arrived, Sam had already fled.

Barbara was wearing her nightgown, her hair hanging down. Her forehead was covered with tiny beads of sweat. And her arm was cut badly and bandaged. She was crying.

I held her in the doorway, trying the best I could to comfort her. She seemed so small in my arms.

"What's he done?" I asked quietly, stepping back away from her. Under her gown I saw her breasts, and lower the dark outline of her sex. I grew hard.

"What's he done, Barbara?"

"Done?" she looked at me bewildered, like a child.

176

I indicated her injury. She was under mild shock, when she noticed the wound she became hysterical. "Go after him! *Please!* He's losing his mind, please!" She broke into sobs, covering her face with her hands, her body shaking, her breasts trembling enticingly under the cloth.

"He can go to hell," I said uncertainly, it being after three and the city immense and the sight of blood making me hate the sonofabitch, and my own feelings about the strength of my loyalty to him confused . . . and, too, wanting Barbara, fuckthoughts racing through my head, distracted by her breasts, her sheer white neck, creamy in the pale light, her collar bone and upper chest pearl in the glow.

"Oh, God! *Do* something. Can't you see, he's trying to die!" She moved against me, kissing me, begging, "*Please,* there isn't time . . . no time, he'll hurt himself."

I held her to myself. "Please," she said one last time, and then looked up at me, seeing in my face my need. "No," barely audible. I steered her to the bed and leaned her back, kissed her, pushed up her nightgown and pulled it away, and pulled my hands across her breasts and down her stomach and into her sex. I threw off my trousers and took her.

It was dawn by the time I located Sam Parsons in Yorkville at an all-night German restaurant, sitting at the bar with a dozen empty beer bottles in front of him, a drink in his hand, pounding the table drunkenly in rhythm to the Prussian anthems filling the room.

"What the hell!" Parsons exclaimed, standing up and waving at me, grinning. And then, perceiving the anger

177

in my face, his grin fell and a look of bafflement weighted with undirected fear took its place. Not fear that I would hurt him, but fear that my friendship was not his, had never been his, that he had been played the fool. Observing his face, I felt sorry for Sam Parsons, with his battered body and his drinking, sorry because I knew he had already run out his life, like his life was ended in the war and he existed as a remnant; like he was some loser just getting the word, a loser with the psyche of an ex-and-failed hustler who has peddled his basket and his ass into his thirties and discovers one day that he cannot score anymore and the terror that the next time he cruises the street he will cross the demarcation between seller and buyer, so he hesitates, unable to do anything, to choose between going into faggotry or dropping, and he cannot choose, so he drops slowly, becoming his terror. Sam was like that, peddling his life, his *version* of his life in books and bullshit stories and suspecting all along, but the suspicion growing terrible, that he had been discovered and judged behind his back. And condemned.

"Sam," I said, not quite knowing how to begin. Barbara was hours away and it did not seem very important now.

"Yeah, stud. Sit down. Have a beer." He waved his hand for the waiter. "Give my friend a beer." He turned again to me, smiling, honestly glad to see me, his confidence returning. He had no idea what I wanted.

"You bastard!" I said evenly, in a normal tone of voice. He cocked his head and frowned. "You are a phony, Sam. You're a coward. Only a coward treats a broad like that."

He drew himself back, glaring at me. "What broad! Barbara? Something happened to Barbara?" He touched my arm, trying to understand what was bothering me and attempting to pacify me at the same time.

"You cocksucker!" A trifle too loud. The waiter stared at us, disapprovingly, from the bar, "I just left her, you prick," righteous, growing confident, Saint George and the Dragon alive and well in Yorkville, "You should've seen her. Sam . . ." I looked up at him and I had to squint because the ceiling light was in my line of vision, I could not see his face, "You are a first class bastard."

"What *is* this?" rising to the occasion, stepping a foot back from the bar and glancing around the room, utterly confused by me, becoming frightened again.

"You cut up her arm. You creep bastard! Her arm!"

"Me?" He did not remember.

"You son of a bitch . . ." I stood to my feet and shouted at him, unloading guilt on his head, from inside my bowels I piled it out onto him, feeling cleaner, better, almost transcendent with each phrase, Barbara's anguish and my indecent response to it egging me on . . . but more than that, Sam Parsons had become, for the first time, a public figure to me. For the first time, his failure and his beat-up head were related to and representative of the world which celebrated him . . . I was beginning to enjoy myself. He stood there defensive, completely stupefied.

"What the *hell* are you saying? What the hell *is* this?"

"You don't *know?*" My turn to act stupefied.

"What are you raving about?" He kicked the bar stool and sent it spinning across the floor. "What the hell has happened?"

That was it, in the tenor of his voice, the edge of fear, not of me, but his fear of understanding what he had done

179

which had brought me bitching and cursing in on him at his hangout. He really did not remember. It struck me then, the man had unraveled somewhere, in his mind were blank, gaping silences. Part of him was lost to him.

"You don't remember?" I asked, incredulously.

"Remember? Remember what!" Cold sober, suddenly frightened like a child awakened in the middle of the night and horrified at being unable to recall where he was. "She couldn't be hurt," he mumbled, more to himself than to me, trying to ferret back in his mind and collect the pieces of time and make memory. "I was with her tonight. We argued. It was over some other dame, a leather dyke I know. We argued. But nothing more, I swear."

"You really do not remember?" more of a statement than a question, double checking, doubt taking root in my own mind. He was very certain.

"Hey," he laid his hand on the back of my neck (and in that gesture, that one movement coupled with the warmth of his palm against the base of my neck, I pictured my old man, walking with my father, the way he used to stroll with his hand riding lightly on the back of my neck, directing me by gentle pressure, occasionally moving his hand up and mussing my hair, long ago) "You must be high on something." He laughed, the doubt dissipated.

"Maybe." I withdrew my head from under his hand.

We took a taxi together to Riverside Drive, in the Seventies, where he owned a duplex apartment. Sam told me to lie down on the couch and he gathered blankets together, and a pillow, searching around for the things I needed, like a bird assembling materials for a nest, tender with me and open, and I undressed to my underwear and

Sam placed the linen and the blankets on the couch. I did a set of push-ups and sit-ups and then I stood on my head and walked around the room on my hands. Sam laughed. I felt very young. I lay on the couch under the blankets. He stood for a moment beside me, a drink in his hand, looking down at me.

"Go to bed, Sam. Before you fall down."

He did not reply but remained standing there. Before he went to bed he reached down and tucked the blankets' edges under the cushions of the couch and kissed me good night on the brow. Like my old man.

"What's that for?" I knew.

Sam shook his head, gazing at me. Finally: "I always wanted a son." His tone was drunkenly sentimental, but what he said was true.

His wife shook me awake, bracelets on her wrists jangling. She was dressed in a dazzling silk print dress, her hair combed back and tied with a red ribbon. She was elegantly tall, thin, dark-haired, very healthy in appearance, athletic. There was a quality manifested in the posture, poised rather in a slouch, like a fashion model, in the way she held her hands together over her purse, there was something in her carriage and in her stance which was foreign to Sam and Sam's world. She possessed, quite simply, *class.* She smiled at me. "It's after three. In the *afternoon.* You and Sam, you love to sleep."

"Is Sam still asleep?" Dumb question, fogheaded, not really awake.

"*Of* course." Snapped reply. "It's daylight yet. It's *early* for Sam." I disliked that, the implication that sleeping late was bad, morally reprehensible, that decent people were like cows who went to sleep early and awoke early. My auntie's attitude in that, superiority defined by rising early. "If you get up, wake him. He ought to be up and about." I was going to ask why, but stopped, considering it none of my business, and, also, she meant nothing snide by it for she laughed, her hand going to her hair, absent-mindedly caressing it.

I scratched my head. "Okay, I will."

"There's food in the kitchen. I made you sandwiches. Sam eats sandwiches for breakfast. And there's coffee, too."

"Thanks."

"I'm going downtown and I'll be back late. Tell Sam and. . . " she winked at me, pulling on her gloves as she did, "try to keep him away from the liquor until after dinner. He drinks too much, and then he gets silly. Like a schoolgirl."

"I know." I meant I was aware that he drank too much.

"I bet you do!" She giggled, and walked over to the window and drew open the draperies. The sunlight dropped through in one chunk. "Good-bye." She walked out.

The light hurt my eyes, that is what forced me off my ass. I staggered over to the window, holding my hand before my eyes, and closed the draperies. I wandered around the apartment, beautifully furnished, from what I could tell. A large room with a beamed ceiling, *three* couches, half a dozen chairs covered in beige and white raw silk. Against one wall was a sideboard on which was a group of photographs in silver and leather frames, pictures of Sam and his wife at a lawn party, in expensive rooms with famous and expensive people. One in particular: Sam with a young Jack Kennedy, together in a crowded room somewhere, both of them grinning at the camera, Kennedy, a trifle uncomfortably, standing arm in arm.

I lit a cigarette and went in search of the kitchen. Located it and put a teakettle on the burner. I made myself a cup of coffee and went back into the living room and through it into a hallway. I checked out three rooms off the corridor before I discovered Sam's bedroom and the adjoining john.

"Get up, Sam!" I yelled, not entering his room, instead going into the bathroom across the hall. I undressed and took a shower. I shaved, pretending as I did that this was *my* apartment, or that my old man had finally struck gold, the big ship had *docked*, by gumbo! this was our very own pad, the furniture, the expensive paintings, the teakettle, *ours!* and I was rising on my everyday in my everyday bathroom and looking at my face—it is not a modest thing to say, but I was *handsome* that morning, shit, yes. For what it was worth—in my big clear mirror and shaving so I could pour French cologne on my skin (that was funny: ball breaking, anti-minty, meanmouthed Sam The Man had a cabinet crammed with foreign perfumes, in handsome bottles like liquid gold) and then putz down to the Plaza Hotel in my Caddie for lunch with a really stacked Movie Actress piece of bush hot after my money and my balls. An American Dream, because I, like every other punk I knew, always guessed that people (especially women) put out for us not because of what we prided ourselves on, what we were, our good qualities, so to speak —being that we were decent sorts—but because of other things extraneous to ourselves. Like toads frightened and puffing up their hide to make themselves appear ferocious and towering to the predator. Like that we were false to reality, hot air priding ourselves on what did not count (and knowing, in the belly, deeply that it did not count— with a lavish house and the rest of it, I would yet be me. Whenever it came, it would come too late for change, essentially). How many sexual losers, the broads with the teacher looks and the scag legs, the boys with a hive of pimples for a face or worse, swallowed the line for a life- time that it was "personality" or religiosity or some other bullshit which divided the winner from the lost? No, it was being born into the club which counted, the money in the bank, the connection, color of the skin, inside and out. By acquiring money, bread, coins, renown, by acquisi- tion people we wanted would *want us* in order to possess our possessions. In the possession make a place for us.

I finished in the bathroom (the way some people use popular songs to recall the big moments in their lives—I screwed my first girl when that song was high on the charts, I received my first promotion when the Beatles hit with that, the Rolling Stones made it big with that record when I was married, that summer—*I* remember *bath- rooms*) and dressed. I went into Sam's bedroom. He was asleep. It was dark. I could see him lying on his side, curled up with his hands thrust between his legs, in the clothes he was wearing the night before.

"Sam, it's after three, nearly four in the afternoon. Have to get up." I crossed over and gave him a shove with my hand. He awoke, barely. Groggy, "Okay." He sat up and stretched. "But not so loud. Don't talk so goddamn loud."

He rolled out of bed. I left the bedroom and walked into his study, which was immediately off the bedroom. The walls were paneled in light wood, like pine, and on three sides were bookshelves, three of which were filled with Books By Sam Parsons. Facing the windows—through which one could see Riverside Park and, sparkling through the leaves, the Hudson—was his writing desk, a long table piled high with papers, books and a typewriter. Immediately above it, attached to the narrow wall between the windows, was a cork bulletin board. The cork board interested me for on it, in addition to a calendar and a mass of notes and telephone messages, was pinned a series of snapshots, yellowing and curled at their borders: Sam in his uniform during the war ... Sam standing under a date tree beside an oriental girl, pretty, dressed in a floral patterned ao-dais, he smiling broadly, soldierly, looking irrefragably *American,* almost Midwestern with his hair cropped short, face scrubbed, the girl unsmiling, her eyes staring down at the ground, her hand cupped in embarrassment over her mouth, like Rosemary, years ago; and another snapshot of Sam with three other soldiers, each with a black cross drawn in ink on the photograph across their chests, under it written: THE JEWISH FOUR HORSEMEN.

I lit a cigarette. I found an ashtray under a pile of manuscript. The room. Cluttered with papers and photographs and books, nowhere for the eyes to rest. And yet each time he worked at his desk his eyes must have seen

185

the cork bulletin board and the girl and the soldiers and the crosses, each time.

In the kitchen I made myself another cup of instant coffee, and made one for Sam. I crossed into the living room and sat down. The water was running in the bathroom. I remembered last night, Barbara's arm and Sam's response to my rage. Thinking about it in the daytime, I concluded that I had overreacted, had inferred things from the situation which were not there. The entire notion of creeping insanity breaking, like an early rash, in outbursts of unremembered violence appeared on second thought to be fantastic. Barbara was an hysterical woman, or subject to fits of hysteria. Maybe the time of the month. And Sam? Memory loss due to booze. It even occurred to me that Barbara may have cut herself in order to force Sam's return that night. I did not think Sam did it. The man drank too much. Nothing more.

I could hear Sam singing in the shower, and it was a good sign, it reassured me to hear him sing, off key, to bellow, for it was a familiar gesture, an expected act. Normal, by God. Sane enough to put my mind at rest.

When I went into the bathroom, leaving the coffee cups in the living room, Sam was croaking out with a baritone *Yesterday.* "Sam!" I hollered, wanting to be heard over the sound of the shower. "You want your coffee in here?" The coffee was a pretext to interrupt Sam, to talk with him and let him know, via the question, that I had thought nice about him.

"What?" he asked, opening the glass door of the shower stall and stepping out, grinning with his hair wet and pressed by the spray tight against his forehead like a headache band. His eyes seemed very bright and very young beneath his wet lashes. I smiled back, noticing only his face. "Sam," I began again, "You want your coffee in . . ." I stopped. I could not go on. Speechless. His *body*. On his chest, on the tender skin beneath his armpits, long, narrow bright red welts there on the side of his chest. Around his groin, on the inside of his thighs (and it was only there, on the inside of *my* thighs, where the idea of pain ever pleased me) beside his sex were scores of small bruises about the size of quarters, like strawberry birthmarks. I had once heard that James Dean was a cigarette burn queen—if true, his legs must have resembled Sam's. There was a lack of randomness to the abrasions and the burns, running like footprints along the channel of the arteries, a contrivance which made them shocking and vastly pitiable and obscene.

"Oh, Sam," my voice shaken and fallen. He understood me, recognized my silence. He continued to smile weakly and turned his eyes upon his body, observing himself almost wistfully, and glanced up at me again. "I know . . ." he mumbled, examining himself with enormous tenderness and, what? with curiosity, as if he had awakened in the morning and discovered them there unexpectedly and could not explain them, and it was the inexplicableness of their existence which concerned him, as if the marks on his body made it foreign to him, difficult to recognize as his own. He glanced at me again, sheepishly, his hands at his side covering the abrasions there, a small, nervous smile playing on his lips, the kind of smile a child uses to indicate embarrassment and the beginnings of shame when caught in the act and at a loss for words yet, despite the shame, perversely proud of his prowess and indulgent of his waywardness. Suddenly shy of me. "It doesn't hurt," he commented, "not badly."

"Why, Sam?"

"Don't know. The war?" He faltered, a bad attempt. "I don't know. I don't even know how I got them. You have to believe me, I cannot remember."

I thought he was lying to me. I was sure that he knew.

chapter sixteen

THE St. James Baths. Basket Days. The end of fall. Hot and humid, the garment district smelling of exhaust and piss near the buildings' edges, and Union Square benched with drunks and Miss Marys lingering furtively by the closed men's room door, the marble temple, *the milk run,* near the children's play area, hoping that habit or need would pull a trick their way while nearby, toward the East River on the border of the Village, the Baths where men without the coins necessary to get inside posed butch in the doorway trying to catch the trade before it entered.

I had never been to the baths in New York, but I was leaving New York, and cleansing, to be Biblical, absolution, was in the water, Living Water, *are you washed in the blood of the Lamb?* The baths would do. The St. James Baths, owned by a charity for boys supported by the New York City policemen's union, was housed in what had formerly been an Orthodox Church. It lured off-duty cops and soldiers and other S&M types and it was renowned for its dirt and male smell and the heavy, muscular, well-hung trade it captured. All-American studs, no nellie Miss Bessies, no flaming queens, no pretty boys. Mortification was its stock in trade, and inside the baths men were conscious of the reputation of the place, the faggot legend of supermasculinity that could transfigure them inside the door, tightening them up; the Athlete Who Lets Other Guys Do Him, the Albee American Dream, the Blond Weightlifter, the Stud-Death Hovering; self-aware they walked slowly, large bodies shiny with oil, naked, penises erect, heads held high like grand duchesses, regal yet graceless and perverse; tough, arrogant, disdainful, absolutely silent. No one spoke.

I went inside and paid for a locker (a private room was $7.50, too much to pay when one left the door open anyway) and walked into the locker, feeling as I walked that I had crossed over and had hit the dirt. The kick was the humiliation. The building had four floors. The basement housed the pool and the steam and hot rooms, and massage room and toilets. The main floor had the cafeteria, the desk, the locker room and the tearoom where the subway-john queens stood guard, safe from the cops. The second floor was one large hall with stalls along its walls and scores of cots in the middle. The third floor had the private rooms, rows of six-foot partitioned stalls with doors, separated by long, dark, narrow halls. The ceiling stretched twenty feet above the roofless stalls in a neo-Gothic arch. The nave.

Downstairs. I hung my robe in the room off the pool. I jumped into the water. I was the only one who used the pool the night I was there. I guess it was not done, it violated some minty tradition. It was an action which carried within it—as walking about with your member covered would—a lack of respect for the higher purposes of the joint which were, in short, fucking, sucking, rimming, and beating the meat. It was an heretical act.

As I swam a little group of admirers gathered at the edges of the pool and watched, one of them squatting on the lip of the pool. Skinny dipping in Michigan. I floated in the water about five feet from him. His body was tight and rigid. His tool hard. He made me uneasy, not in the sense of being a sexual threat; the uneasiness came from the intensity of his lust. When you hustle, the john has an intensity about him, but what is operative in his excitement is not only the sexuality of the encounter—which, I sometimes think, is a minor factor—but the potential for violence. Violence, and the hint of the possibility of sudden death, animate the eroticism in that situation. However, at the baths, it was pure sexuality beyond individuality, and the assumption that I was utterly like him. That it was free.

The guy squatted on the tile edge of the pool staring at me glazed, his cock in his hands, pulling off. He shot off into the water and then leaned over the edge of the pool and lapped up his sperm floating there. He stayed where he was, leaning now on all fours, his face inches above the water, red as his blood flowed to his head, his ass up, as if he were expecting some movement from me, as if I were to repay his gift to the water. I looked at him unable to imagine what cue I had missed, what part of the ritual I was to play. I was at a loss to know how to begin to respond. As I watched, another man, also in his late twenties, taller than the guy who sent his seed into the pool, came up behind my admirer and squatted in back of him like a dog and began licking his ass, lapping it loudly.

I got out of the pool and headed for the steam room. As I did I glanced back, like Lady Lot turning again to the City, and saw one still balanced over the water as behind him the man vigorously jabbed his finger in and out of his ass while he rubbed his own cock with his hand. Lot of fags in America, Sam had said. Goddamn right.

The steam room was crowded, like Macy's on a Saturday afternoon. It was dim and so fog-filled that I could not see two feet in front of me. I walked to the far corner and sat on the marble ledge, the hot steam feeling great on my skin—and I was totally beyond sexual desire, overcome by boredom and a drooping fatigue—and I leaned back against the cool wall, drops of warm water from the overhead pipes falling on me, and watched as two men paced in the center of room, emerging from the steam to stand a moment in front of us (I shared the ledge with two boys) sometimes holding their pricks tightly in their hands, sometimes standing with their hands on their hips, their legs spread, like Marines in recruitment posters, their meat swaying with the movement of their pelvises; sometimes they stood pressing their cocks against their lower stomachs rubbing them up. Every few minutes a man would come out of the mist and thrust his cock against the kid next to me and the kid would slap the cock hard, the man would groan and move away. Again and again. Whack! Groan!

What surprised me most about the St. James Baths was the size of the organs—enormous—and the massive builds of the men and the emphasis on silence and exhibitionism, the watch queens moving musclebound like huge mechanical dolls feeling themselves up. I found the place anti-sexual, overstated, ahuman, lacking any semblance of personal interrelationship, except on a highly contrived physical level. It made hustling seem warm and very human in contrast. It was not dirty sex as much as it was symbolic sex at the St. James, the sex of promise and fantasy where the players moved in prescribed patterns as in a religious pageant. No one spoke, silent as hustlers, for speech, that carrier of reality, prevented the mind from play and loss. They were rigid because the poses were limited, the repertory of sexual gesture painfully bound to a kind of masturbatory theatre, a dream world where something lay precious and hidden in the movement, finally unpossessable, beyond reach, creating an image to take home and replay in the mind and to exhaust. The stance and the postures were inner-directed. They acted independently of the watchers, existing by themselves. And what I learned, and it was essential for me to know and accept it if I was to grow up complete, was that the freedom lay elsewhere. It was not to be found in the unreal masque of the gay hunt. It was not in the streets. But it was elsewhere. No, not in the straight world, but somewhere farther, tougher, without ease. Somewhere inside.

There is a thrill that comes from walking, weighing your member in your hand, and moving it toward another man's face or ass, a symbolic, beautiful violation directed against oneself without expiation. Freedomless. Trapped in contrivance. The coming was in the play of the mind one acted out monotonously, now a slave, now a master, now a sergeant exposing his virility to the ranks, the Presi-

193

dent ordering massive death with ease for the deaths are, of necessity, unreal to him, paper death, a master exposing false virility, his power, losing and confirming it at once. Yet lingering in the play. To themselves and for themselves they acted. Player and audience simultaneously, using others to support one's fantasy, appropriated by others as a prop for theirs. Objects becoming transcendent.

Sitting there, with the two fruity numbers on the end playing chopsticks with each other's prick while each stared ahead appearing not to notice what his right hand was doing, like subway riders oblivious to their neighbors, faces placid, emotionless, I thought of Chicago, and coming in from Evanston on the El and going to Reilly's Baths off Rush Street, once traveling there, the first time, with handsome Parker. I was sixteen that summer and the place was full of kids and men who needed money or needed to give it. It was a clean place and it had about it a rough tenderness, a sense of play and good times like in a boys' camp. It was a clean place, and I have nothing bad connected with it to remember. We boys would sit on long benches in the locker room waiting for a man to notice us—like boys in the Middle East in peg houses sitting on benches fixed with two-inch pegs to keep their anuses distended—Middle Western, middle class, good family boys, and I thought then that the men at Reilly's were old, old Northwestern and Chicago and Garrett students, undergraduates, younger than I am now. I thought them old. And for a couple of bucks you let them blow you or let them do it in the English way, fucking you between the thighs. But your sweet rosebud—virgin children—they never touched. Or your mouth. And, in a subtle way, it

was innocent and it was not hustling for it was uncon-
scious and it came not out of any need for money, it was
not selling, but it was a game the gang did together, without any sexual label placed on it, and receiving the money
was one of the rules. It had none of the traumatic effect
that selling meat does the first time it is done, beyond
final resistance, with all the options covered and delimited
to itself, done out of physical hunger. Done because there
is no other choice. I am not trying to rationalize away my
being a hustler. God knows. I am only telling how it comes
about. There is no other exit one can see.

St. James was worse than Reilly's in Chicago. It was less
human. No smiles or tenderness. No human pursuit. Christ,
even hustlers are *involved* in the act. They communicate.

The steam room was getting overcrowded. And it stank.
Someone had shat on the floor.

I went into the toilet. Three men stood before the
urinals jerking off, watching each other as they did, like
the candymakers lined up like bulls in a barn in the john
at Grand Central; while they pulled off, a man, a black,
crawled on the floor behind them smelling and rimming
their asses.

I pissed in the wash basin. I wanted to keep my ass to
myself.

Upstairs the opened door stalls were occupied by young
and middle aged men lying singly on cots, some rubbing
their pricks, or lying on their stomachs with their fingers
pressed to their assholes. Most were absolutely still, eyes
closed, like corpses. The ones on their backs would be
sucked, those on their stomachs fucked if their luck held.

Regulated. Systematized. Ritualized. The money changers and the non-commercial whores and the publicans had the temple at last. Like hunks of meat ready to be put to any use.

I walked around observing, being observed. In one of the booths, on a narrow cot, the light dim, lay a fat man. I stopped in front of his door. He lay on his back. "Motherfucker," I said, for in my mind he stood for the buyers. I went inside. He rolled over. He said nothing.

I went up to him. "On the knees," I said. He climbed onto the floor, making a grunting noise, loving the slave role, and took my cock in his hand, caressed it, spit on it, licked it, sucked it in and out, while I looked away, up to the ceiling painted blue with angels with trumpets circling in flight around a judgmental Christ on a cloud with a staff mounted by a cross in his left hand, his right on the head of a child.

When I had come, the fat man lay back on the floor, and said something, his eyes plaintive.

"What?" I asked, bending my head down.

"Piss on me," he whispered, his voice hoarse.

I looked at him a moment, undecided. Why not do it, go to the farthest end of the road so you are not bound to make the way again. Why not? But I held back and grew angry. Golden shower queen. "I aint no faggot," I said, and, to prove it to myself, to prove I was a thief before I would be a faggot, I reached down and ripped off the gold chain he wore around his neck. I left.

Going downstairs, on the landing, a soldier stood naked in boots, dog tags, looking down severely at another man, a blond—Albee's vision—a young boy, maybe seventeen, whose head he held in his hands and moved rhythmically back and forth in front of him.

Enough. I considered the need for triumph and command and the strange ways in which young men have been twisted, made to turn away from themselves. Manhood. The need to affirm it and possess it and abuse it and transcend it. Manhood burlesqued and sought after and elevated like the Host.

chapter seventeen

I HAD never seen palm trees before. Not in person. I had seen them in war movies (war pictures, along with cowboy pictures, were my favorites) about the Pacific where Sam Parsons fought, and I had seen them on postcards of the Bronx Botanical Gardens at the Union Cigar Company store near where I lived, but I had never seen them in the flesh, so to speak. It was the palm trees which made Los Angeles seem unreal to me. They grew in tall rows along Sunset Boulevard. They stood like sentinels above the costly foliage of Beverly Hills.

At the Los Angeles airport I stopped for a drink at a bar called the Tahitian Village. It was a phony tourist cafe with plastic palm fronds making a roof over a lean-to in the Eastern Airlines Building. I sat at a table under the thatch awning and looked across the lobby through the wall-high windows out to the street. There the real things were, four palm trees reaching to the sky, their trunks crusted with rows of terraced spines, like pickets, a small, wispy bouquet of leaves at the top in the sunshine shaking in the wind. It was one beautiful sight, reminding me of pictures in Sunday school books of Jesus H. entering Jerusalem before the Government hanged him, little children tossing palms, like petals, at the feet of his donkey. Or paintings of the South Seas where colonials sat in wicker chairs on verandas bordered by the fringes of jungle palm, sat in the high noon before the dense green fanning themselves and waiting.

It was difficult for me to accept and understand the existence of a place where it never snowed.

I decided to leave New York *before* I hit the baths. It was seeing Sam with his body wrecked. It was having been too long in one place and learning, finally, that I was being changed badly by the place. Not that hustling was bad. It was neither good nor bad. It was that rage kept appearing in me and I could not understand its appearance and my response to it was violence. I saw Sam and I understood. That could be me. To take punishment in your body, to arrange it, and not to give way before it—in some difficult way that had to do with the assumption of manhood.

Anyway, after I decided to leave, before I went to the St. James Baths (my farewell appearance) I called auntie. I did not call to ask to return to her boardinghouse in Evanston. I called auntie to check in, like boys do from summer camp, called to let the folks at home know things are okay. Haven't drowned or got poison ivy. The scout master is leaving my tushie alone.

Auntie said my father had written one letter on the back of a postcard showing Knott's Berry Farm. He announced that the Big Ship had arrived in port. "I hit the pay dirt at last!" The Pot of Gold. He gave his address as the Hollywood Imperial Skyview Hotel on Sunset Boulevard. I flew into California the following morning.

I ordered a rum punch (another first for me) and heard the barman at the Tahitian Village tell me I had an accent, which nobody had ever told me before. Being told made me feel self-conscious and foreign. After I was told I mumbled when I spoke to him.

"You from Nebraska, fella?" That was what he asked.

I said No.

"You *sound* like you're from Nebraska, or some place. Got that kind of *farm* accent." Evanston was no farm.

Evanston. Auntie mentioned that sister Lily was training to be a piano tuner. "Whole school of blind folks learning to tune pianos in Oak Park. Regular closed shop. Don't let normal people do it, from what I understand." It was a terrible thing to hear about sister Lily, about her doing that, in the back of my mind always I assumed she would have an operation or a miracle drug or even a faith healing which would give her the light. Piano tuner! My God, that was hopeless. Sister Lily spending a lifetime with a pair of pliers and a tuning fork leaning over piano strings.

I stayed at the Tahitian Village bar for about two hours watching the people move through the electric eye doors, the outside heat and the eyestinger air pouring in when the doors swung open. I was collecting the resolve inside to get up and meet my old man. Now that I was actually in Los Angeles it did not seem such a great idea, everything considered, to see him after so much time. He might be a real mean sonofabitch, had to expect anything, since what you remember when you were five years old about your father is not always true anymore. I really did not believe that he had made the Grand Killing and was able to set us up like kings of the fucking hill. Never happened to anybody I ever knew, not in America anyway. I did not believe that at all. I simply wanted to see the bastard, deep inside I knew I could not leave without looking the man over.

I packed a suitcase in New York. I brought along a two dollar bronze Statue of Liberty and a towel from the Pacific Moon Hotel to prove I had been on the island. I called Coretta and Sam Parsons to tell them that I was leaving. "When will you be back?" both asked. And to both I replied, "Couple weeks." Lying when I said it, knowing I would never be back. Another promise. I flew out of Kennedy Airport, watching the city from the airport bus. Through Queens. It was like Chicago. Only time I had been off Manhattan Island and somewhere else in the city. Off Manhattan the town was like every other place.

I could have stayed in New York no way. Finished in that town. The scene in the baths frightened me, facing what I had become: the All-American Boy. I saw myself slipping toward the edge with no grip in sight. Better to see my old man, sooner or later you want to. It's in the blood. I would think about myself then, try to figure me out. I could not do that in New York.

I remembered what Parsons once told me about the time he nearly murdered his wife. He came home late one night after falling in two bar fights earlier that evening (saloon brawls were small and precious war battles to him. It was being in the Pacific Theatre again) and staggered into his apartment blind drunk and disheveled. He turned the phonograph on very loud to kill the ringing in his ears. He foraged around for more booze, enough to quiet him. His wife had locked the liquor up. It outraged him. He pushed into her bedroom and bullied her demanding drink. She was awake, sitting in a chair staring at him.

"Where's the scotch? Where's the goddamn scotch?"

She looked at him. She hated him. "Where have you been, Sam?" Inquiring like a mother.

"Out with the boys!" Defiant.

"You're a pretty sight, Sam," looking at his torn clothes and swollen face, *"You look like a rolled faggot!"* The last curled over the tongue and hissed.

With that he began punching her about. That was a crazy fucking thing for a man to do. And that was where I was moving.

As I should have known, my old man was bullshitting about the hotel, at least about where the premises were located. It was not on Sunset Boulevard. It was on *Holly-wood* Boulevard. That's some difference. The taxi drove me along the freeway into Hollywood and along Sunset to Hollywood Boulevard. I expected to see Movie Stars on the streets. I expected to see a city. What I saw was a gathering of small towns strung like plastic pearls along the freeways, and empty sidewalks and many cars, and the Hollywood Hills rolling up behind us, their banks and bluffs littered with pastel colored houses and blue-green pools, and below the Hills, below Sunset, the Los Angeles city basin stretching to the mountains, a bowl with a few high buildings and lots of ticky-tack houses blurred under a hazy yellow-gray-brown cloud.

The taxi stopped in front of the hotel, the place being a narrow doorway between a movie theatre and a cafe with a sign above the entrance reading, in broken neon letters: *WORLD FAMOUS HOLLYWOOD IMPERIAL SKY-VIEW HOTEL, one flight up.* Outside on the sidewalk were small, ersatz gold stars with actors' names etched on them. *Richard Barthelmess* was memorialized under the movie marquee. Going inside I thought, where else should my old man go but to a town which claims a cemetery and a berry farm as major cultural monuments. Man, he *belonged* in L.A., along with the Hollywood Wax Museum and the camp gold stars in the sidewalks and the place lousy with religious fanatics and thrill killers and wouldbe actors in skin-tight levis and body shirts hustling along Hollywood Boulevard.

The lobby. I was back at the Pacific Moon in Manhattan with aging winos sleeping it off on torn vinyl upholstered furniture, a ceiling fan (that was the only authentic Hollywood touch) turning above me, trailing a tail of dust behind it like a gauze banner, and two hustlers waiting for sundown in the corner. Hollywood Boulevard was hustlers' row. I spotted the brothers the minute I exited the taxi, saw them when I climbed the stairs and entered the lobby—one greeted me by glancing up, picking his nails, and readjusting his posture, the pelvic area for a moment moved. I passed to the registration desk, and he settled down again in the heat.

It is a small point, but I will belabor it anyway: the desk clerk was an astonishing human, and he represented in his person all of the zany contradiction and offended, misunderstood dignity—the charlatan ruffling his feathers protectively in anticipation of rejection—the clutter of second raters, losers, role players, frauds, gimmick experts, dispossessed failures from the rest of the continent who landed in California in hope of Success. The Good Life. People in California talked to me about the good life there, and by that they meant principally the weather and the anonymity. One failed alone, and others worked to protect your illusions. The desk clerk at the Hollywood Imperial Skyview Hotel. Picture him: a small man, about five five in elevator shoes, wearing a three-piece *heavy* tweed suit in the Southern California heat, a gold chain dangling between the side pockets of his vest, a rosette in his lapel, a long cigar, like a redneck chaingang boss in a thirties movie, crammed in his mouth—above it, elegantly gray, faint, like thin angel hairs fallen above his lip, a pencil-thin moustache to complement the greased slick Continental hair, graying too and thin, combed back in a style considered sexy when Cesar Romero made moving pictures about gay Havana with Carmen Miranda and her unspoiled fruit. He stood behind the desk, the counter immaculately clean, the area behind the desk a world removed from the lobby. The same peeling white paint. The same smudges. Yet incredibly neat, as if *in spirit* it was the Plaza in New York.

I walked up to the desk and he eyed me, giving an audible sigh of resignation, pursing his lips.

"May I help you?" His hands folded together on the desk counter. A look of offended superiority. He spoke in a trained voice, like an actor.

I asked him for my father's room number.

"Mister . . . Mister, hmmm, let me see . . ." walked over to the file case behind him, flipped over a few cards rather grandly and returned with a card in his hand.

"Yes. He checked out, oh, about a year and a half ago. He owes, let me see, yes, he owes forty-one dollars, to be exact." He said it, the money part, with a kind of petulant condescension as if he had been reminding me of the money due for years.

"Do you know where he is?" I ignored the money part. I did not have it.

He looked at me a moment, and then he shook his head. And there was something in the restrained, prim way in which he gestured which made me think he was gay.

"He was a salesman, wasn't he?"

"Pardon?"

"I say, the gentleman was in sales, was he not?"

"You mean my father? Yeah, I guess so, if that's what he said. I haven't seen him for a long time."

He nodded. "You're his son? He spoke of you. He said you were an actor. On Broadway."

"No." I wanted to get the address and leave.

"Excuse me?" He hadn't heard the answer.

"I said, No, I am not an actor."

"That's odd. Well, his forwarding address is the Haven of Rest Mobile Homes Park. That's in Topanga Canyon." He wrote it down on a slip of paper for me.

"Thanks." I turned to leave.

"Where are you from, are you from the South by any chance? Many Southerners come into L.A. I think your father said the family was from the South."

"Nebraska," I answered.

"Oh." He was disappointed. "I once was in business in Atlanta. In burials."

Almost out the door. His last words, "By the way, tell your father we are going to take him to court. It's illegal not to pay rent in California. And, if you have the time, drive over to Forest Lawn, a magnificent . . ."

The Haven of Rest Mobile Homes Park, Inc. was not actually in Topanga Canyon. It was situated just outside of it, in the valley on the road to Santa Monica, in a hilly, low ravine on the valley's rim. I arrived at dusk, the taxi having to swing off the freeway and onto another road and finally off that to a dirt driveway which circled through a pine arbor to the camp entrance. I saw it and it reminded me of the Okie camp in *The Grapes of Wrath* movie, the one Henry Fonda had to run from, only it wasn't that classy.

The road ended in front of a shack with *Office* on the door. Beside it was a map mounted on a board. HAVEN OF REST RETIREMENT VILLAGE, INC.

Trailers parked along gravel paths with names like Magnolia Mews, Daffodil Drive. Most of the trailers were very small affairs with little gardens or vegetable patches bordering them, tiny square cement slabs large enough for several chairs and a small table in front of them; some had awnings on the windows, some had picket fences. The entire camp was overgrown with trees, and flowering bushes. By each of the trailers was a small nameplate with the title of the home and the occupants: Mr. and Mrs.

Johnny Smith, *Golden Years House;* the Peter Joneses, *September Song Cottage,* and so on. My old man lived in an aluminum trailer with rusty steel bolts and a round back, about the size of a tree house. It was located on Poinsettia Place. It was called *Journey's End House.* Nice.

My old man was slouched outside his Journey's End trailer on a canvas director's chair next to a skinny old lady sitting on another director's chair, and they were fanning themselves with folded newspapers like people do in the Middle West when they sit at night on their front porches and watch the cars go by. He looked in bad shape, slumped down, his chest sunken and covered with curly white hair. He was nearly bald, save for a rim of long white hair on the sides of his head which gave him an Old Testament Prophet look.

The old woman was withered, with bobbed blue hair. Her head and hands trembled. She saw me before he did, and she leaned over to him, making little squeaky word-like sounds, and directed a shaking finger toward me. He glanced over at me, and then bent forward asking her to repeat what she had said. Then he looked at me full, giving me his Howdy-partner-let's-talk-business grin.

"Hello there, young fella. A little late to be peddling wares in the park tonight. Rules forbid it after five." Good-fellow laugh. It was my suitcase which made him read Salesman. And it was the sound of his voice unchanged which made my stomach flutter and my face smile. "Father!" I shouted. And I was happy.

He squinted his eyes, stared a moment, let out a whoop. "Angel!"

"I was so *close* to it. Goddamn! I had it in my hand, in my *hand*, I tell you. A million dollars!" He waved his hand in the air to emphasize how close he had come to the million bills, and his hand hit the yellow antibug light hanging from the low ceiling inside the trailer. That made him mad, so he made a swipe at the light, and missed it and in the process stood up tall and hit his head against the ceiling.

The three of us were sitting around a table top suspended from two chains on the wall. Mrs. Mable Balls (the lady's name, pronounced BAA-Halls) was asleep in her chair, her eyebrows twitching. The conversation started outside on the cement terrace and then moved inside when the neighbors complained. It was stuffy inside, there being no windows, and both my old man and I were dressed in our underpants to fight the heat. "At *least* a million. Surefire cure for cancer! Discovered by an eminent doctor of podiatry in Mexico City who built himself this world famous clinic down there where dukes and kings, *millionaires!* come by the thousands every year to take his pills. By the *thousands* they come, Angel, come to get the Mexican Miracle Drug Treatment. Mable here," he nodded in her direction, and went on, a little disconcerted by the fact that fifty percent of his listeners were dead to the world. "Mable is a walking testimony to the cure. *Look* at her! Picture of health, by God, and to think *only two years ago she was given up for hopeless* by the greatest specialists in the world!" Asleep, anyway, she looked like a corpse. But that was not how *my* old man saw her. He envisioned her as a seventy-year-old gold mine, a female Lazarus to be trotted out at county fairs to push

208

the Cure. "And *I* owned the American *rights!* God DAMN!" He dropped his head in his hands and fell into his chair, his elbows on the table top, his head shaking woefully, dramatically, and stared down at his yogurt de-coagulating in the dish. He had an on-again, off-again bleeding ulcer. Lived on yogurt and goat's cheese. He paused, examining the yogurt.

"So what happened?" Like a jerk, I had to ask.

"Hate the stuff," he replied, speaking about the yogurt.

"What happened with the cure?"

"Well, what do you expect?" giving me a sidelong glance and his There-is-no-justice sigh. "You get a little edge on life, an inch ahead of the fucking game and they got to knock you down. They got to fuck you up. They got to . . ."

"Who?" As if I didn't know.

"Why the Government, *that's* who! Or the fat cats, the goddamn, lousy cake-eaters! The bastards. *Some*one! You got to fight the bastards always, or sooner or later they screw you good." He made an Italian Fuck You gesture with his arm. He stood up again, hunching his shoulders and lowering his head to avoid the ceiling. "Goddamn hot in here. Dump. Spent my life living in a series of lousy dumps."

"Let's go outside."

"Sure. Why not. Fuck the neighbors."

We walked outside leaving Mable asleep in the trailer. We sat down in the canvas chairs. There was no breeze. "Dump," he said, pointing backwards with his thumb at the trailer. "Live like a school of stinking sardines in a can. Aint fit for human habitation nohow."

"Should we wake Mrs. *BAA*-Halls or leave her sleep?"
A civil question. It made him suspicious.

"Wake her? Are you crazy? The old thing needs her
rest. Got to keep the assets alive. Christ, you can't tell
when she's awake anyway. Until she moves or sneezes.
It's eating away at her insides. I give her six months." He
said it grumpily, like it was her own goddamn fault she
had only six months left on earth.

"What eating away?" Cancer, for sure.

"It aint *cancer*, if that's what you think! She *cured* of
that. It's distemper or some fucking thing. Forgot what
the Mexicano doc called it. But it aint no cancer." He
stood up again, irritated, his mind preoccupied by Mrs.
Balls' mortality.

We walked away from the trailer down Bluebird Boulevard, under the yellow antibug light bulbs strung on
wire like Chinese lanterns above the bushes, the night
heavy with fragrance from the flowers, the air motionless.
We settled on a bench in a pine arbor about ten yards
from Journey's End. I heard a dog bark. I was back in
Grant Park by the lake at night with him. Long ago.

"That's why I got to hurry. Six months and we have to
bury the evidence. *Nobody* believes in cures. Shit, even
if you got the evidence it's hard to convince the bastards.
No wonder Jesus had so much trouble. Nobody believed
him. Mable, she's got doctors' letters and certificates from
Mexico *proving* she will live forever on the drug. That is
too good a thing to pass up."

Not once, since I arrived, did he inquire why I was
there or where I had been. He rapped on like it was the
day after he had left Chicago. As if nothing had happened

since. Only remarks he made about the past were to note that "your aunt is a sonofabitch," and "little Lily has got a bright future, she sure does. A great career ahead of her." That was all.

"Mable and me, we set up the Orange County Miracle Cancer Foundation, Inc. And we tried to incorporate another thing, the Ma*yoo* Clinic of Orange County. Couldn't get it through the bureaucrats down at Records. I got me a retired Army Major and a preacher to sit on the Board of Trustees of the Foundation, for a consideration, of course. That made it look legit, to the public. It was always legit to me. I'm telling the truth. But you need a few *professionals* to give *any*thing class. One thousand bucks a week we were hauling in, honest to God. Think of it! We were in business, in *practice* for a month. At a thousand a week. Never made more money in my damn life. And then the goddamn-lousy-cocksucking-lying-no-good-sonofabitch-fucking Feds moved in. Commies! Anti-Free Enterprize! Anti-Medical *Science* government of ours! Shit, the FDA bastards shut us down! Bang! Put a lock on the door, like we was debtors. Humiliating, I tell you, goddamn hu*mili*ating! And you know why?" He turned to me, pounding my shoulder, outraged, "YOU KNOW WHY? *I'LL TELL YOU WHY! Because of the medical monopolists!* that's why!" He paused a moment to let me absorb the shattering Truth. "The American Medical Association protecting their goddamn copyright on bilking the American public. Yes, sir! Hauled our asses into court, me with the damn ulcer acting up, Mable coughing and wheezing like a basket case in court. . . . For Christ's sake, I thought the poor old thing would breathe her last in the courtroom, and would *that* have looked lousy in the press. Didn't look good, no, sir. 'Physician heal thyself,' that was what was going through the mind of that shithead judge. That was a year ago. Humiliating."

There was a *long* silence. He brooded over the defeat to enlightened medical science at the hands of the courts. I spoke up, asking the obvious, something always to be avoided. "Done anything since?"

"Done anything *since!*" He boomed it out. "Nothing but fight the entire United States Government with my bare hands, Mable and me. Fight for the freedom of religion." He was off and running, and listening I knew he had given the spiel a hundred times before, most likely on late night radio talk shows, *Tell us, Doctor, about the Communist Conspiracy against American medicine and religion* . . . his Bible School had awarded him a post-bankruptcy doctorate in medical science, to go with his divinity degrees. "We are incorporated under the laws of the State of California as the First Church of Religious Medicine, Inc. And we got about a hundred thousand miracle pills stashed away in town, and we can get more. We use medicine in our religious worship, I aint lying, like the Indians in the desert. If they can snuff dope why the hell can't we peddle a few miracle drugs?" He had me stumped. Why not, Mr. President? "No motherfucking FDA cop going to halt the progress of medical science, not while *I* live and breathe. . . ."

Every line, the last for example, which appealed to some higher *Reader's Digest* kind of cultural value, was declared in his most earnest, obnoxious, sententious manner. It came to me: my old man was not a person, he was a parody. And he was back peddling on the street corner where my mother had found him, hawking his salvation-for-a-fee, his voice traveling to her broken by the wind.

My father met the lovely Mrs. Mable Balls in San Diego two years before, where the widow was struggling to keep her small, bankrupt traveling circus above water. My father, never willing to give a sucker an even break, hounded the Widow Balls up and down the coast from Chula Vista to Laguna Beach to Garden Grove. The old lady never had a chance. He signed her traveling circus as a client at two hundred a week plus expenses, and as a generous man became its publicist. Somewhere on the highway between Miramar and Poway the sheriff caught up with the circus trucks, impounding the tents and the animals and the costumes and the games of chance for bills past due. The old man had given it an honest try. But he was moving against titanic odds: the two lady dwarfs were lesbians, and years before in Bonita, outside San Diego, the little women got bombed and made a pass at a local girl. Overnight the circus lost the patronage of the good people of Bonita and every town up the coast, the Knights of Columbus, the VFW, the Legion, the women's clubs, all the service organizations who keep small circuses with two dwarfs and a couple clowns and a handful of animals, plus one aerial act, in business turned against the entertainers. The scandal followed the widow and her publicist like a plague. After the circus closed came the widow's cancer and the Cure. They never married, although they lived together.

My old man referred to the widow's "artistic spirit" in

discussing the collapse of her tents. "Like a lot of things in show business, here today, gone tomorrow. You work your ass off for the smell of the greasepaint and the roar of the crowd and then the bastards *turn* on you. And an *artist* like Mable, well she takes it hard. Barely said an audible word since."

I stayed with my old man, sleeping outside the trailer under the awning on a cot, the Statue of Liberty bronze standing on a chair near the cot to intimidate the neighbors. My father's idea. In the mornings he made the rounds of the other trailers trying to sell the old and enfeebled in the retirement colony mail order tonics, therapeutic beds, orthopedic shoes, earning a commission in the process. Rarely made a sale. The man simply did not convey a sense of trust, to say nothing of solvency. He had Promoter written on his face. And his heart was not in it, his vision being on grand schemes to make a million on some birdbrain invention, some promotion, a con.

Sunday morning. About dawn. "Wake up, kid! Come on, Angel, we got work to do! Rise and shine! Up and at 'em!" Mister Sunshine banging my cot with his foot, speaking in a loud whisper and slapping a newspaper against his leg. I opened my eyes. He stood at the foot of the cot in his underwear grinning down at me madly.

I sat up, blurred. He began to pace around the cot, gesticulating crazily about some looney idea that had hit him hours before.

"It came to me this morning." Hoarse whisper, glancing around to see if anyone was listening, "My stomach was acting up something terrible. I spit and see blood. Blood on the goddamn pillow." I tried to speak, upset about the blood. He continued on, silencing me with his hand. "It's nothing. Been going on for years. So I got out of bed and went and got the Gelusil and drank it down to soothe the belly. Can't sleep. I turn on the light and start reading the paper. *And do you know what happens?*" I stood up and stretched. It was going to be a long morning. "IT COMES TO ME! THE GREATEST IDEA OF MY LIFE! FUCKING *A!* READ!"

He threw the newspaper over to me. It was the religion section of the Los Angeles Sunday *Times.* An article about a minister. *"The Rev. Ronnie Roland, formerly of Baltimore, Maryland, announced today the purchase of the Eldorado Theatre on Wilshire Blvd. as the permanent sanctuary of the Hollywood Christ the King Church. The Rev. Roland founded the church a year ago last May in a series of devotional Sunday morning meetings in his home in Burbank. Since then the Rev. Roland's church has grown to a membership of five hundred. . . . The Rev. Roland is an admitted homosexual, and he founded the Hollywood Christ the King Church as a religious home for the homosexual community. The Rev. Roland said recently . . ."* It went on for two columns more.

After I read it I handed the paper back to my father. I was pissed, for this he wakes me at dawn, to read about some fag minister with a church.

"Well?" he was beaming, standing in his underwear beaming in anticipation of my enthusiasm. I did not understand.

"Well what?"

"We are going to . . . *I* am going to put Rev. Roland on the map! Goddamn! Can't you see it! This country is *lousy*

215

with faggots, millions of them. Millions! This preacher can be bigger than Billy Sunday, bigger than Aimee, bigger than Jesus himself. Why I'll book him into the Los Angeles Coliseum, into Madison Square Garden. I'LL BE HIS MANAGER! We'll . . ." *No, old man, no,* I thought, laying myself back on the bed, *enough of the gays, enough, old man. Too many cold parks, too many. Tired now, old man. Want to be left alone. Want to stop the goddamn buying and the selling. I am worn through, papa, I am beat.* "We'll start a weekly television program, on the network yet. And a queer book club and . . . and a *queer correspondence college* and day camps and, shit, why not? a *political party for fairies!*"

He went fuming on like that, pacing around kicking up the dust, the sun moving higher in the sky, getting warmer, and I lay back on the cot and put my face into the pillow and for the first time since I arrived I remembered Willie and I wondered where he was and whom he was lying with. And if it was for free. And I said to myself, tomorrow you get your ass out of this goofy town and away from your goofball old man. The guy is bananas.

Ten-thirty that morning found us getting out of a taxi cab under the marquee of the Eldorado Theatre on Wilshire Boulevard, my old man dressed in a shiny black suit, a blue tie, white shirt and polished shoes. To finish the undertaker look, he sported a white carnation in his lapel. From a distance he looked good, if bereaved. Up close, well, the shirt was frayed, the suit spotted. I sensed he would not pull it off.

On the way to the church in the taxi I asked him why the hell he thought Reverend Ronnie Roland would contract him as business manager. "Ministers don't have business managers, papa. They aren't movie stars or something." He found my remarks astonishing.

"Are you serious? What the hell do you think Judas was if not J. C.'s business manager. What do you think all those miracles and the walking on the water, all that crap, what the fuck do you think it *was,* for Christ's sake, if not publicity gimmicks. The feeding the people on that hill there. Boy, he *knew* what he was doing. That was the best trick in the world, to send ten thousand fed people, fed free yet, home to tell the news about his soup line. Jesus was no dummy, kid."

"But Ronnie Roland aint Jesus."

He looked at me. Paternal disappointment in the thickheadedness of the young. By way of reply, "Kid, you sound like your mother more all the time. You know that? I remember the year we were hitched I got the idea of staging a concert of Kay Kayser and Wayne King. . . ."

"Wayne who?" Never heard of them, and by the tremolo of his voice as he breathed their names I knew I was obligated to be impressed.

"Good God, are you *dumb.* Goddamn dumb kid I got me. Kay Kayser and Wayne King happen to be the greatest, the most im*por*tant bandleaders, *entertainers* if you will, of all time. Their very names on the marquee of a theatre, say the Paramount in New York, was enough to bring a horde of rich women to the box office. *Biggest thing in the world!* Now my idea was to create something called the Cavalcade of Bands, with Wayne King and Kay Kayser getting their old groups together, maybe reviving Kayser's Kollege of Musical Knowledge game, understand?

sending them on a tour of the world, ending in the White House at a State Dinner."

"What happened?" Again the obvious.

"I made contacts with the men, informally you see, and was about to sign them to long-term contracts when your *mother*, God rest her soul, when she got cold feet. Wouldn't come across with the cash for the stationery. Good God! You can't sign nobody without recent *business* stationery, any fool knows that."

He glanced over at me. I knew what was on his evil mind: hit the kid for stationery money.

"We'll see about that tomorrow," he said, meaning the stationery, "after we whet Mister Preacher Roland's appetite. We sign him. I know how to handle fairies. Got to use kid gloves, be subtle. Slip the noose over real quiet." He winked at me conspiratorially.

"Nobody else? Your public relations career was limited to the bandleaders, nobody else?"

"*Business manager extraordinary!*" He was into the role completely, the taxi had become a Rolls, and my cynicism was dismissed out of hand with an indulgent, patronizing humor, the kind reserved for neophytes and outsiders. He was convinced in his bent mind, think of it! that he *almost* pulled off the Cavalcade of Bands, and that he was about to sign Ronnie Roland, D.D., to an exclusive contract and pack the Los Angeles Coliseum for homosexual revival meetings. Bananas, like I said.

"There was Miss Aimee," he continued, enjoying himself, "The Reverend Aimee Semple McPherson, the greatest woman of her time. What a woman! A veritable monument to American womanhood. Talked to her once in an elevator in Portland, Oregon, at the hotel there ... she was conducting a series of revival camp meetings in the area ..." he glanced over quickly to see if I were swallowing the line, "... and we prayed for a moment together. She always prayed before her major decisions. She used to say, 'Brother, always fall on your knees before the Almighty, then put your hand in the till.' Profound. She wanted me to produce her play, *Come Forth!*, even suggested that I might consider playing the lead ... it was about a dead man, Jesus I think, who came back from the dead. A musical. I was tied up at the time with university work and whatnot. ..." He fell silent, bemused by the memory of Aimee pleading with him to take her on as a client and he, overwhelmed with Educational Commitments, turning the distraught woman down. "Tried to fit her in, but, you know, a man can only do so much at one time. ..."

When we arrived at the church the pre-service coffee hour was in progress. It was like a gay bar, only more openly minty, hundreds of inverts jammed into the vestibule of the church like nellies in the back of a truck by the Hudson, drinking coffee, dishing one another, cruising nervously, fluttering, making small talk and eyeing the studs, even eyeing my old man and me, impossibly straight in appearance, my father playing it as respectably ministerial as possible under the circumstances, I wanting to fade into the woodwork. Not because I was embarrassed, but because I was guilty. And I was acquiescing in the old gangster's employment and contempt of them. I was sensitive enough to know that.

As we moved through the crowd one of the gays fluttered

his eyelashes at my father. "Hello, sister!" he hissed. My old man blanched, his dignity attacked. He pulled me aside. He gestured to indicate to me the hissing queen and the crowd. Perturbed, yet keeping Business foremost in his mind, "These fairies got no money. These are the *little* fairies. *Clerks!*" He was right.

Inside the auditorium people were crowded against the side walls and standing in the aisles. A photographer from a magazine was taking pictures of the congregation and as his camera moved the queens camped it up for all they were worth. The choir processioned in. We sat near the front. The service began with prayer.

The choir delivered an opening anthem, something about marching to Zion, and the congregation joined with them in "Jesus Savior, Pilot Me." It was like being back at the Salvation Army in New York, only without the tambourines and the sandwiches. An Assistant Minister came to the front and read the announcements about various "community" (i.e. gay) activities, teas, protest meetings, bookstore specials, and the like. A few more hymns were sung, my old man getting nervous over the delay in the appearance of Ronnie Roland. A middle aged, devoutly trembling sister rose to the pulpit, his robe flowing magnificently around him (when he stepped to the platform he lifted the hem of his robe elegantly, preciously, and his face reddened as his eyes fluttered over the congregation) and trilled, in castrato tenor, *"The Stranger of Galilee . . . come ye who are weary and tempest tossed, his perfect salvation see, he'll quiet life's storms with his Peace, Be Still, this Stranger of Galilee. . . ."* My leg fell asleep.

My father began to slide inch by inch protectively under his seat, thoroughly discomforted by the schmaltzy worship and the cloying boys, feeling displaced and threatened (and in him, I think, the impulse to preach. Part of his discomfort was having to sit there without being able to address the congregation. My old man loved to preach), the Reverend Ronnie Roland bounded to the pulpit, grinning at us all wildly, tall, rather handsome in a rough way, with a Maryland accent and idiom speaking of years pastoring rural churches. The man *was* impressive, very professional in the sense of being completely in command of himself and of his audience. "Welcome, children! We're all brothers in the Lord! Amen! God is good, don't you know! *Gay* is good! Hallelujah! Gay is beau*ti*ful." He moved into his sermon like a plow into the earth, talking about how homosexuals were persecuted and denied, how they were comparable to the early Christians for their ethic of love, and how the established churches, corrupt and hypocritical, condemned by God and reason, were silent on the war and yet piercingly loud in their denunciations of love between men. The fellow was an effective preacher.

My father listened intently at first, his head resting on the palm of his hand. He commented once to me, "This guy is *good*. Ought to be a carnival barker." He was serious. Soon, however, having heard enough, the judgment made, he gradually withered in the pew, bored, sitting through the communion service half-asleep as the homosexual congregation passed in single file in front of us to kneel before the minister and have him place a pastoral hand on their necks ... *I am not worthy* ... and a wafer

221

to their mouths and a cup to their lips ... *this is the body and the blood* ... and give a chosen few a brotherly kiss. *The Body and the Blood.*

In the vestibule, waiting as the congregation filed out, each stopping momentarily and self-consciously to seize the pastor's hand, some to kiss him on the lips like pilgrims kissing Our Lady; giddy, pathetic, dying queens; rumbled, displaced and desperate rough trade moving to the streets; victims become His Train. My old man standing to the side astonished, even baffled, taking it all in hungrily, piecing it together, computing, adding it up; growing nervous, damp, his collar and suit wilting, stage fright drawing the blood from his face.

With the theatre empty my father lurched at the preacher in a rush, sweat breaking on his brow, and grabbed the preacher's hand in a vise-grip, never letting go, and like a cold-sweat junkie hitting you on the street for a handout to purchase smack short of theft, oh God, short of that, implacably demanding, like that my old man went blindly into his routine. He babbled it out *intensely,* madly. The man was wholly without subtlety, my father.

"Great speech! You are a great preacher, young man, I mean it, swear to God from the bottom of my heart. You'll be big, I tell you, big, *big!* like my dear friend *Sister* Aimee, may she rest in peace. (Rev. Roland did not know how to take the *Sister* Aimee line. He smiled tentatively.) No, *bigger,* big as my close friend Billy Sunday himself, very close friend of mine. Really. They *both* were my intimates, I tell you, very close to me personally, if you know what I mean. *Family* friends. My son here, he remembers fondly their visiting our house on occasion, don't you son?"

(I nod. The preacher had placed one hand on top of my father's and he was visibly attempting to disengage their hands, to no avail. The grip held, my father disregarded me and plunged ahead.) "But you got to think big, you need *management*, Father ... (my old man confused in denominational address) ... and *I am what you need!* I *watched* you, Father, as I watched and studied two former clients of mine, Kay Kayser and Wayne King ..." (My father enunciated the holy names slowly and paused a second to let the significance of his friendships sink in. Nothing happened. Ronnie Roland stared ahead unmoved and unimpressed. He looked scared, the preacher, as if it had just occurred to him that he was captive of a bonafide waco.) "... I studied your crowd, your *congregation*. Listen, I'll be honest (Roland scanned the room for an exit.) Your crowd is a bunch of little fairies, that's all you got. *Poor* fairies. You got to get the *big* queers in here (Reverend winced. My old man plowed ahead unperturbed.) You need *big fags!* You listening? The fairies with the money up there in Beverly Hills, you got to get those fairies in your campaign. (Roland was blanching, backing away, grinning sheepishly like someone who suddenly had lost his marbles, mumbling incoherently. My father, unfazed, shouted on.) Now *I* can put you on the map! MAKE YOU THE BIGGEST THING IN THE FUCKING WORLD! You don't *believe* me! I HAVE DONE IT BEFORE! I will book you into Albert Hall. (A pause. No response. My father glanced over to me, sweating profusely, worried. He concluded that Roland was an ignoramus.) A-L-B-E-R-T H-A-L-L. That's in *London!* LONDON, ENGLAND! (Nothing. The preacher had

223

gone completely blank.) Got to stage meetings in Paris, in Rome, in New York City, meet the President, a close friend of mine, *he owes me some favors* ... in Madison Square Garden, we'll put on the biggest show in history, go to the *White* House, have our pictures, *your* picture taken with the Prez on the White House steps, *it'll make the front page of the Chicago Trib!* (The old man was over the edge. Desperation, like boils, was breaking out. His face began to twitch.) Listen, preacher, there is no MONEY with these fairies you got here. *NO MONEY!* Understand? Got to get on the television, got to get where the big pansies can support, no rich fairy will come in here with all these fags you got. THEY CAN'T AFFORD TO BE SEEN HERE WITH THESE QUEERS!" Roland turned suddenly, brusquely, broke my old man's grip, leaving my father babbling into empty space. I helped the promoter outside.

"The goddamn *dumb fairy!* DUMB! DUMB! DUMB! Won't amount to nothing! He *needs* me. The dumb fairy *needs* me!"

Returning to the Haven of Rest Mobile Homes Park, Inc. my father said very little in the taxi, complained a few times about the excessive heat, unbuttoning his shirt and pulling off his tie as he did. He was sweating profusely, unnaturally, and he stared out the window mumbling to himself completely disoriented by the experience. "The man's blind. An idiot." And: "Let *anybody* be a priest these days." And: "How can a man kiss away a million bucks? Must be crazy." He went on in that vein, shoring up the argument that he was better off without

224

that half-wit preacher gumming up his reputation, to agent a loser like Ronnie Roland was beneath his professional standards. The man was bitterly, destructively disappointed.

At the trailer Mable Balls asked him where he had been.

"Saw a client. Big deal in the works." That was all he said, and drifted outside. A few minutes later Mable brought me a trembling plate with a tuna fish sandwich on it and my old man a dish of poached eggs. She stood in front of him and waited until he had downed them, putting up with some spoiled bitching in the process. Then she forced two glasses of warm milk down his belly.

"Can't figure it out." We were outside. I sat on one of the director's chairs, he lay sprawled on the cot, breathing very heavily, moving his hands nervously in front of his face as he spoke. Mable was inside on the bed. The two of us were stripped to underwear, fanning ourselves with portions of the religion section of the Los Angeles Sunday Times. "Don't know where I went wrong."

"He's an idiot. Don't let it bother you. He'll probably think it over and call you up tomorrow."

"Who cares? It aint that anyway. It's *LIFE*." Back to auntie's upper case. "All my life I have come so fucking close, you know. And then, just when I thought I had it . . . don't understand it. Maybe it's me. This country. Only country I ever understood and I can't make it break for me. Understand? It just won't open up for your old man. A man shouldn't be driven to scheming, you know what I mean. A man should have decent work to do. Angel, I tell you honestly, you got to have a few friends you respect around you and work to do that makes sense.

Otherwise nobody can survive. You just can't survive without both of them."

Man, I really felt for him. He was confessing failure and I did not like hearing it, and it was important that I listen, that I hear and make response. But I had no answer.

"I'm going to look for a job. Tomorrow. You wait, we'll set ourselves up proper." I said that to cheer him up, and that was the first time it occurred to me that I might stay on with my old man and help him out. It was not that I felt sorry for him, that wasn't it. I was tired of running. I was tired of being outside. With your father, if he is a good and decent man, after a point you are never required to prove anything. You *are.* I mean, simply being the son was sufficient. I was comfortable with him. I thought he was probably an old fool or worse, but a nice kind of fool, a very native kind, a good natured one. He was harmless. All his fulmination came to nothing. Harmlessness, that is much to say for a man in America. That he hurt no one, even when he tried.

"You don't have to do *that,* Angel." The idea of *regular* work, like normal people do, instinctively repellent to him. "We'll manage. Something will come up, it always does. You need a vacation, kid, coming all the way from back East. The weather change and everything." He pulled himself to his feet, tiredly, preparatory to going inside the trailer, and he walked by me and laid his hand on my neck and ran it up my head, mussing my hair, and down again, squeezing my shoulder. I felt like his son.

At the time, I really think that at that moment I appreciated the appropriateness of the gesture, and the resolution it contained. It was like the completion of a circle.

It was sufficient and necessary to what had gone before in my life, and what immediately followed in his. I do not know if he expected what was coming, but if he had known he could not have made way for it better. For, quite simply, at that moment, in that gesture, I loved my old man. What was remarkable was that it was such an easy thing for me to give way to.

On the steps of the trailer. On the steps of the trailer he stopped and gripped his neck, his hand moving slowly, almost indifferently to his throat, and he made a gagging sound in savage, absurd contradiction to the elegance of his hand's gesture, a gagging sound like someone who has been kicked in the throat makes. He drew his hands to his face, and started to cough fiercely; with his hands covering his face like a lace fan, like Jerusalem palms, he coughed fiercely, coughed like a person desperately trying to force water from his throat and lungs, and coughed and then, buckling forward, for a moment tittering, shuddering like a branch shaken, he began to vomit. I knew then it was over. He fell off the steps. I tried to break his fall in time, I tried to catch him, but he was heavy and I was too slow, and he hit the ground with a muffled thud and for the last time almost formed a word, his throat clearing momentarily in the fall. He fell off the steps and landed on his side. He landed on his side, his hands gripped over his mouth, distorting his face, his hands over his mouth and gripping his facial skin and twisting and pulling it. His eyes rolled back in his head and his eyes were open but all white, like white oval pebbles washed on a beach, like white pearls inside a shell. When he lunged off the steps of the trailer I ran to him, as I saw him sway and teeter on the steps, I shouted his name. His hands and the front of his chest and his neck and his face were blood wet. Only there was no visible wound.

He survived less than an hour. He said nothing. Internal hemorrhaging broke his life. And he was gone.

the end

JUST got into San Francisco from Los Angeles, got in like
a New American Immigrant, broke, owning nothing but
what I wore, and believing San Francisco to be the *place*.
"It's the last trolley stop," my aunt had warned me, "You
can't go no further." *Down,* she meant, thinking it evil.
I walked from the bus terminal and saw my first cable
cars on Powell Street, and continued to walk until I
reached Union Square. It was approaching ten o'clock at
night. I was tired. On the run. I carried my suitcase, and
in it my bronze Statue of Liberty and the Pacific Moon
Hotel towel stolen in order to have something to prove
I had existed once on Manhattan Island and survived,
learning little. I was excited about being in a new city,
decided in my mind when I made it up about leaving
Los Angeles for good—it was a dumb town, Los Angeles.
What else can I say. It was an easy place to leave—that
I would never settle anywhere, that I would be a rolling
stone, maybe a sailor and see the world. At the bus terminal I stopped and had a chicken salad sandwich, which
cost me 95¢, and a cup of coffee, and counted my money,

holding it in my hand between my legs under the lip of the counter so nobody could see (about thirty-six dollars to my name) and next to me at the counter were two blacks new in town—really from the South, unlike me with my Southern-but-Midwestern accent—jiving about the View. They wore black shirts and on the back of their black shirts (should I be bathetic once more this late in the game and admit the awful truth, that seeing their young hard backs sculptured through their shirts, that in seeing them my mind—as it does with such ease, if with little grace—bound itself to the memory of Parker's back in the early evening as we walked along that burial lake with the sweat pouring down his dark skin, and my removing my shirt and with it, gently, wiping the sweat from his skin and in the movement of my hand on his back, the feel of his muscles turning under my shirt under my hand as he moved, in the rhythm of his walk, that I was tempted there to admit what I have never admitted: that I loved Parker deeply and without guilt, loved him enough to bend for him. There, it is out.) on the back of their black T-shirts was written BORN TO LOSE. My old man would never have driven confession that far, however true. Nor would Parker. Or Andrew. Nor would have Coretta. Losers all. It was bad form, having that spelled out across your back unambiguously and clean. Never let the bastards know they've got you by the balls, to quote the quotable Sam Parsons. Or they'll never let go. Jiving in their black shirts, I left the bus terminal and hiked into Union Square. I recognized a gaggle of johns. No more, I' said to myself, aint you ever learned your lesson, cocksucker. No more, never, ever, no more, no more. I moved through the Square and began walking north, at least I think it was north, for I ended in Chinatown, which was a nice place, as far as Chinatowns go. Better than New York's yellow ghetto. I found a rooming house—*Canton Palace,* I was fated to spend my life in palaces, not quite up to Jack's father's place in Wales, but close, close as I ever got to a pleasure Dome without a Kubla Khan (a poetic reference there, evidence that I am not bereft of all general culture). One thing you can say for the Chinese in San Francisco, they keep their establishments *clean,* thank God. My room was very comfortable. It possessed a very large window overlooking the street, about as big as the window in the Rector's house in Chelsea, and outside of it was an exquisite, wrought iron grill in the form of two dragons devouring each other's tail. If you crawled out on the window sill you had yourself a balcony of sorts, and a view: down the hill a few blocks another larger hill began and at the top of it was a building with an elevator on the outside of it, like a glass drain pipe, that went up and down all night with people riding in it; outside, if you did not smoke too much, you could smell the Bay in the air. It smelled like the Hudson at a distance on a good night. On the street were neon signs advertising various things in Chinese script. And people. Unlike Los Angeles, there were actual people walking the streets after five in the afternoon. That's something to be said for a town. By the time I checked into the Canton Palace it was late, pushing midnight. The boy at the desk was a hippie named Long Legs who had yellow hair and a yellow moustache and kept sniffing something from a paper bag. He told me to walk north and I would hit North Beach,

231

where our people lived. He was right. In North Beach I had another sandwich and an organically grown salad, all for 45¢. The cafeteria was called the Minimum Daily Requirement, and it had little white, round tables and wooden Victorian chairs in very bad shape, and it was full of sleepy kids reading paperback books and rapping while a radio played classical violin music. A good scene. A block from the cafeteria was hustlers' row, I noticed but I went on by, just like the sanctified Christian ("Can you say that, can you say 'Methodist'?") my auntie raised her little All-American manchild to be. I was moving fast the first night, trying to keep my head occupied by playing Tourist and sightseeing the sights, trying hard not to think, not about New York or Evanston or Parker (lay off my mind), or Willie (lay off my mind) or losing my lousy losing old man. Keeping loose. I went for a drink at a bar in North Beach, having decided quite by chance on the bus ride up from Los Angeles, I think we were rolling through Salinas when the Revelation came, that I was destined to be an alcoholic so I might as well enjoy it while I was young. The bar was a very non-tourist place, a neighborhood saloon where the bartender ran an open house, runners, pimps, my kind of folks. Above the bar was a poster showing Saint Peter's Square (that's in Rome, as my old man would say, in Rome, Italy), and another one picturing the Pope riding on a golden throne and giving a papal blessing to the camera. Hanging between them and rustling in the current of cool air coming through the windows from the Bay far away were two slips of old fly paper, yellowed and curled, covered with insect corpses. I had a double scotch and water, and then

232

another. I drank standing like a man at the bar, like a man at the bar, interesting, *like a man at the bar*. Next to me was a middle aged fellow already into too much booze. I stood there listening to him talk to the man next to him, who was obvious in his disinterest, I was fascinated by his speech, his intelligence and his undisguised anguish (that is the word) and there was something to his embattled dignity which reminded me of Sam and of my old man, in the few staggering good moments of his life when he was not shoveling out the bullshit onto whoever else happened to be in hitting distance, and something, too, about him which was of America. That was what came to mind listening to him. And I cannot tell you much of what he said, not too specifically until the end. This I know: he spoke of wars and killing and woman and age and of giving birth. He was really laying one on, boozewise, his speech already grown thick and his mind wandering through bogs of sentimentality and nostalgia from one topic to another, my mind following him like a child skipping after the Piper, I, too, open once more to sentimentality and deathful words; I placid and comfortably fatigued, feeling winded after a race and somehow escaped, free; a survivor come to tell, come from the dead, come back to tell you all, I shall tell you all; he raged on, his friend ignoring him, bits of his talk sputtered out like pieces of a breaking puzzle gathered by old hands in bad light, gathered and unfitting; as he talked his right hand traveled up the side of his jacket, near the breast pocket, and played absentmindedly with a small, perfectly round hole, like an eye in the khaki cloth, which he described melodramatically as a place where a Kraut's bullet zinged

233

through clean and harmless, the bullet being an excuse to discuss the cause of war, or rather the causes, the various causes mounted in words in the bar, like insects dangling on a pin, variously contradicting each other as he enumerated them, he contradicting himself, nevertheless as he spoke encompassing the earth in his heroics; his eyes darted nervously about the room never fixing on anything, several times his vision passed by me and I smiled into his eyes and, for a second, a smile would flicker on their edge like a light out to sea and then it too would pass moving on; the eyes moved like the eyes of a head on speed, like Tutu's eyes, following the motions of the people in the room, their movement as forms independent of content, blue collar boys, rough trade, and I was convinced soon that he was keyed up for a rumble, rigid inside, moving on—minutes now—into combat; his conversation, like an S&M act, flitting between the poles, master to slave and back again, from the giving to the receiving of death, and in between the meaningless buttends of his life. He looked over at me, shaking his head ironically, wondering at the speeding ineluctability of his life; he looked at me and after that look, when he held it a moment too long, that is, when he noticed me and accepted my presence and right to hear, after that he began speaking in my direction, for my ears. And when he began to speak to me, I, in turn, began to be conscious of my aloneness. He laughed, and as he laughed he pulled his hands through his hair and I saw, on his right arm, on the upper part of his arm, *America The Beautiful* tattooed there above an anchor all in blue, like it had been formed there at birth by a miracle, the arteries arranging themselves precisely.

234

"What did you want to be? I know you're not what you wanted to be, nobody is." I said I wanted to be a fireman. I could not remember wanting to be anything in particular, unless it was to be black. How far we have come. "I'll drink to that!" he raised his glass, "To the firemen, God bless 'em!" I laughed as he shouted the salute. "Should I tell you a secret," he leaned toward me, asking in a very low voice, his tone confidential, almost shy, the tone by itself stripping years from him, making him younger than before. We had moved to a small table off the bar by the window facing the street. An hour passed. He spread himself over the table, bending toward me, his large arms powerfully embracing the roundness of the table at its rim, pulling his hand through his hair, looking across the table at me and glancing away, his eyes narrowed, a wry, indefinite smile breaking on his face, "Should I tell you a secret? Listen," barely above a whisper, his hand fallen on my hand, pressing it, "I nearly killed a man once. After the war. I killed many in the war. That is part of it, that is understandable. This was later, in San Diego. I almost killed him, a kid, eighteen, what, and he made a pass at me. Outside, in the sunshine yet, do you believe it? in the daytime. So close I came. I swiped him with my hand, if I had held a knife . . . the intent was there. But the secret, the secret, you see, is the way he looked at me when I swung at him, the surprise when he knew, in the swing, that someone wanted to end his life, and, this is it, that he did not care. Knowing it, he would make the pass again. I'm not projecting. Moments later, he said, 'Do you want to do it?' Isn't that something, that dumb kid. What balls he had. What chutzpah! I could . . ." I missed the

235

rest of his sentence, although it must have been funny for he laughed and stood up and headed toward the men's room, laughter peeling from him as he walked, laughing like an idiot in a tale as he went. The bathroom was located to the side of the bar, and as he walked by the bar he passed two spades, young men, who were drinking together, glowing they were, drunk-happy, as he went by them he slapped them on the shoulders, laughing. And I knew he was after a fight, you can tell that in a man when he has been drinking and his ability to cover has worn thin, and I remembered something Parker had once said to me, "Never been a coward, man. Always willing to fight, if it came to that, use my body in a fight. That says something about a cat, about his manhood." I nursed my drink, waiting for my companion to return, and I glanced out the window to the street; two old women sat next to a fish cart gossiping and reading beads in their hands, watching the traffic. An argument broke out at the other end of the saloon behind me. It sputtered for a few minutes, I trying to ignore it, and then I heard my friend (at that point the term became applicable) shout out, *"You niggers!"* Glass broke somewhere rooms away from me. For a second I did not turn around, did not move to inquire, but my body tensed automatically, the heart speeded up and for some curious, undiscovered reason I remembered the queen on Eighth Avenue wailing at the body of her fallen hustler, wailing like Rachel mourning her dead children uncomforted, and I felt immeasurably sad. It was as if nothingness as a being (a contradicting image) pushed into the room like a suffocating presence, and we grieved. I did not turn around. Do not involve

yourself, stay back. *"You motherfucking . . ."* A stool sent
flying into the mirror behind the bar, making an enormous
crash. With that I jumped to my feet and discovered that
I did not want to move. My friend was backing away
from the two blacks, one of whom held a large glass ashtray in his fist, and my friend was gesticulating wildly
with his hands to warn them off, creeping away as he
did. They jumped him. They jumped him, both together
making a thudding, cluttering swoosh sound, the sound
of someone jumping on a mattress with pieces of glass
jingling on top of it. It happened so quickly that what I
saw was him standing hunched and then overwhelmed,
the spades knocking the almighty shit out of him, and he
shouting, *"Fucking bastards . . ."* the teeth gritting in the
sound, courage there, goddamn it, wrongly beautiful
courage. I was a coward in that I hesitated, not immediately wanting to respond, not with the blacks involved,
sensing that my friend wanted to contain the violence by
himself, welcome and possess it, become it compulsively,
that it was decisive, this occasion, in charting what he was.
That it belonged to him: defeat. For a moment I hesitated,
my decision as to taking sides was paralyzed and confused. It was a split-second reflex which revealed the
cowardice, now it was taken into consciousness and suspended there. People had abandoned their tables and
started moving, some in a rush for the door, others toward
the fight. I pushed my way through to my friend, still undecided, my body deciding for me, or the situation deciding for me. The blacks had raised him against the edge
of the bar, so that his feet (he had lost his shoes) did not
touch the floor, and they were pounding their mighty

hands (I am tempted to say, majestic hands, for my reaction to their movement was one of awe, reverence before the sheer fact of their strength. It was, in a perverse way, a beautiful display of human brutality. It was both appropriate and horrible. It was elegant and graceful.) into his stomach and face while scores of men stood in a tight circle watching, white men, yet physically uncommitted, yelled absurd encouragement in *Italian* to my friend, as blood ran from his face, some of it landing like spilled wine at his feet, blood streaming from his left eye, coming down his cheek and in the stream pieces of white matter visible to me. For a moment I stood depersonalized. It was unreal. I could not take it in, not the blood, not again. The image that came to mind, watching the blacks rip into him, and he lying back almost passively now, his arms making ineffective, almost comic reflex motions toward his face, moving inches up and down his chest like puppet hands, his legs swinging stupidly against the bar, the image was of a man being raped. "Motherfuckers!" I shouted, the cowardice passed in the beating, in the actuality of it—for a moment it was unrelated to me, like a mysterious ceremony performed for others, a performance—the sounds, the fact of his taking it *alone*, deciding by virtue of the sheer imbalance of the odds against him (and even if I had not heard him talk, not known him at all—perhaps it would have been easier then to come to his side—even if it had been Parker and Andrew who acted as the attackers, *if only!* who were offing him, even then by instinct I would have sided against them. For me that was a long awaited truth come true. That was making

238

good.) that it was on his side that I belonged. And that was determined not without ambiguity for it only held for a time as a working conviction, it was nudged into indefiniteness once I entered the fight and took the first blow. I jumped the black who was laying into his face; and doing it I was worried suddenly about my friend's brain, about what their hands were making of his brain, damaging beyond repair . . . for a moment, too, I considered my face, proud of my face, handsome, you know, but that too was lost in the fight, the worry . . . the black I had jumped bent forward to throw me; as I was about to be flung over the bar, I caught sight of my friend's face bloodied, torn up, but his right eye open and full of terror and excitement, and I think, no, I am positive that he saw me. I am sure that he did. Over the bar I went like a sack of cabbages, smashing my head against the cabinets lining the wall; making it to my feet, circling to the side and around to the front where he was again, impossibly, standing on his feet, blind now, tossing pathetically inept, misdirected punches, like a girl scattering rose petals at a wedding; one of the blacks met me as I almost succeeded in reaching my friend. Right in the face. Flash! Bright light. Down in a lump, my nose bleeding, up again, seeing my friend, my old man lying on his side in the dust of the ground holding his hand blood wet against his face, Big Tom smashing me down, the room ringing, twirling, incredibly shrill, shrieking noises in my ears, the black leaving me to join the other spade working over my friend, general fighting breaking out over the saloon floor. Again I was up pushing back toward my friend, having difficulty drawing my breath, pains in my chest, grabbing a beer bottle off the floor and swinging it at the black who had laid into me, *even the balance,* missing his head, God, missing it by a mile, the bottle bouncing in my hand on his shoulder. I was so appalled at missing that I stood dazed for a moment before my own ineptitude, the bottle held ridiculously at my side, while the spade turned, looked at me, gave me an asinine grin, and sent his fist into my wide-open face; I saw him raise his fist, *slowly* with extreme care, I stood there like a dummy watching as if it were a dance rehearsal, watching as it came up and across, meeting me just below my left eye. I lay on the floor smelling the sawdust and the spilled booze—the smell was sexual—and hearing my friend groan on the other side of the bar, his groans increasing and diminishing in volume, moving into bellowing wails, howls, and then dropping in whimpering groans, his groans at last muffled and unexpectedly high, unearthly high, as if his throat had been crumpled, breath wadded upside the pipe; I lay without power to aid him, will spent, detached and phasing depersonalized beyond concern, my mind welling up with masses of trivia, what I had to do tomorrow, did I leave the water running, all the while knowing I was betraying him. That was what was crazy, that I felt guilty for doing what I could not help but do, for lying semi-conscious on the floor and not dragging myself up and getting murdered. But that reaction, guilt, may have come to me after the fact, for, unlikely as it seems, looking up from the floor, my head swimming, my left eye closed, feeling blood run from my nose and cheekbone down my chin, cooling there, feeling it drop cold on my hands, lying there and looking up blurred, for a moment between the struggling forms, the men moving fast in front of the windows of the saloon (twelve small leaded panes, before the first row, in neon, *Budweiser*) I thought I saw Willie. Several seconds I watched him standing outside staring in at the brawl with his face distorted by the imperfection in the glass, not seeing me, I too low and peripheral to the action, in a navy blue pea jacket, the collar pulled high, his hair falling over his ears, the fringe of his hair, like priceless flax, resting like a wave on the jacket collar, on his head a seamen's wool blue knit cap, in the summertime dressed for winter seas, the cap like binding, blue swaddling, around his skull, above his green eyes. "Willie!" his name lost in the noise, breaking glass, the police sirens, my friend coughing desperately and swearing insanely on the floor beside me, released yet refusing to leave hold, and my guilt over Willie, over them all—sharp, unbitter, so *like me*—flowing into and compounding that over my hesitation to side with my dying friend, and in the guilt something of my manhood disfigured and splintered like glass. "Willie!" and he was gone. Sirens. I got to my feet. I headed toward the door, forgetting my friend in pursuit of Willie, looked back briefly to observe him lying on the floor, his head and neck supported by the brass rail, his nose and cheeks, his entire face mutilated and covered with blood, like Willie's face distorted through the glass, my beaten friend's form oddly shoved out of place, puffed, unrecognizable, his eyes beaten closed. Outside, cool night, standing in the street, the cops, three, four minutes later an ambulance, the stretcher being carried out and a doctor slipping in beside it, the door closed, my leaning against the wall of the saloon outside, suddenly feeling sick, wanting to vomit, wanting to cry, trying to form Willie's name with my lips, to call him. But his name would not come.